A Candlelight Ecstasy Romance ®

IT WAS A SENSATION UNLIKE ANY SHE HAD EVER KNOWN . . .

She clenched as wave after wave of shivering passion began to wash along her nerve endings. With every movement, every caress he was making it manifestly clear he wanted her to abandon herself completely to him. He wanted to ravish her senses, seduce her, to make love to her in a way that left no room for any element of cool distance. Kali knew a kind of primitive fear at the back of her mind. If she allowed herself to be swept into the whirlpool of desire she would be running a risk such as she had never really known. That same tingling, exciting fear warned that this man didn't seek merely a satisfaction of the senses; he wanted to *possess* her. He wanted to embroil them both in a blazing affair which, even if it lasted only one night, would burn itself into her very being.

A CANDLELIGHT ECSTASY ROMANCE ®

CONFLICT OF INTEREST

Jayne Castle

A CANDLELIGHT ECSTASY ROMANCE ®

Published by
Dell Publishing Co., Inc.
1 Dag Hammarskjold Plaza
New York, New York 10017

ISBN: 0–440–10927–2

Printed in the United States of America
First printing—April 1983

To Our Readers:

We have been delighted with your enthusiastic response to Candlelight Ecstasy Romances®, and we thank you for the interest you have shown in this exciting series.

In the upcoming months we will continue to present the distinctive sensuous love stories you have come to expect only from Ecstasy. We look forward to bringing you many more books from your favorite authors and also the very finest work from new authors of contemporary romantic fiction.

As always, we are striving to present the unique, absorbing love stories that you enjoy most—books that are more than ordinary romance.

Your suggestions and comments are always welcome. Please write to us at the address below.

Sincerely,

The Editors
Candlelight Romances
1 Dag Hammarskjold Plaza
New York, New York 10017

CONFLICT OF INTEREST

CHAPTER ONE

"Kali, for God's sake, do something! He's going to ruin the evening! The only reason he's here in the first place is because you made me invite Gwen. I should have known there would be trouble. And this evening is so important for Sam!" Amanda Bryant glared beseechingly at her friend. "I swear, if that man causes a scene and wrecks my carefully planned party, I'll . . . !"

Kali Havelock took a last, delicate sip of the innocuous white wine she had been nursing for the last hour and smiled soothingly. Her smoky gray eyes reflected a cool satisfaction which went unnoticed by the attractive but agitated Amanda.

"It's all right, Mandy. Everything's under control. I'll handle Lang Sterling for you."

"You'd better! He wouldn't even have been here tonight if it hadn't been for you! I won't have Sam's political future jeopardized by something as stupid as a brawl under my own roof!" Amanda shot a seething, blue-eyed glance toward the double doors which opened from the crowded, glittering living room onto the entrance hall beyond.

"Mandy! How was I to know the man might cause a scene over Gwen?" But Kali's protest was only halfhearted. She'd carefully set up the situation and the fact that it was bearing fruit made it difficult for her to spend much effort pretending innocence.

"You knew her ex-husband would be here tonight and you also know the two of them have been carrying on a love-hate affair since the divorce last summer!" Amanda closed her neat little teeth rather fiercely on the remainder of the accusation. "Forget it. It's too late to do anything now but try and stop the situation from escalating! Where did Gwen find that Lang Sterling, anyway? He doesn't look at all like the usual easygoing types she's been baiting Aaron with for the past few months!"

"How should I know where she found him?" Kali asked honestly. "I have no idea how they got together. I can give you one very good reason why Gwen Mather's been encouraging him now that she's found him, though."

"You mean some reason other than the usual one of taunting her ex-husband?" Amanda gritted, flicking another glance toward the open double doors. She was watching the progress of a man as he made his way through the fashionably dressed crowd. Lang Sterling was moving purposefully toward the entrance hall beyond the doors. Gwen Mather had disappeared through those same doors only a short time earlier, followed subtly by her ex-husband. The small parade was adding up to a dose of high drama totally unneeded in the home of an aspiring candidate for political office.

"Mr. Sterling," Kali explained gently, "is soon going to be a very rich man. He's already begun living on his expectations."

"He's going to inherit a fortune?" Amanda demanded

quizzically, her lovely face swinging back toward Kali with a frown. Amanda was always on the lookout for potential contributors to her husband's campaign.

"He's about to *earn* a fortune," Kali corrected automatically, setting down the wineglass with a decisive little movement. "And I suppose it's time I told the man just who is going to pay him all that money." She smiled once more at a totally perplexed, totally anxious Amanda and moved to join the exodus of highly select guests.

"Kali? What's going on here?" Amanda hissed nervously. "What are you up to tonight?"

"Business as usual," Kali told her with an amused glance over one velvet-covered shoulder. And then she stepped calmly into the throng of expensively dressed people which filled the room and stood between her and the double doors at the opposite end.

The black velvet of her long-skirted evening suit cut a dark swath through the array of beautifully attired men and women around her. It wasn't that her clothing was any less well-designed than that of the other guests but there was a certain cool, conservative tailoring to the crisp, fitted jacket which shaped her small, high breasts and narrow waist. The sophisticated sweep of black velvet skirt stopped at ankle length, revealing the gold heels of short, cuffed, black dress boots. The delicate flash of gold at her feet was softly echoed by the nearly hidden lamé stripe in the black silk blouse under the jacket.

Even if she had been wearing flaming red and purple, however, an onlooker would still have been aware of the air of aloof, controlled intelligence about Kali Havelock. It was evident in the strict coil of the heavy braid which was wound at her nape. The dark, jungle brown of her hair gleamed in the plush lighting of the room but there was no softening effect.

The smoke-gray eyes were faintly tilted at the corners

13

but any touch of impishness which might have resulted was squelched by the boldly styled frames of her glasses. There was humor in the smoky depths of her eyes but it was as aloof and controlled as the intelligence.

The curve of her lips, tinted with burnished brown-gold tonight, conveyed a hint of subtle sensuality but it was as restrained as the rest of her.

The firm lines of nose and chin provided a setting for the combination of features which came together in a face which Kali had long since accepted as unextraordinary. At the age of thirty she had developed an extremely pragmatic view of life and of herself. So, while she knew her face wouldn't inspire warfare in her honor, she also knew its lack of pink-cheeked softness was an asset in business. She would have liked a few extra inches of height, finding five feet four inches occasionally insufficient for creating that forceful first impression she favored, but her figure was slender and she wore her clothes well. She ought to, she reflected from time to time; she spent enough on them. They were a business investment.

Her lack of height was making it difficult to follow the progress of the man ahead of her, but Kali knew her quarry well even though she'd never met him and the merest glimpse of his dark, auburn head now and then was sufficient for her to keep track of him.

A group of potential campaign contributors parted conveniently just as Lang Sterling moved through the double doors. Kali wasn't far behind. She emerged in time to see him start deliberately up the stairs leading to the second story of the Bryants' charmingly redone Victorian townhouse.

That would be, she realized grimly, the same route taken by the tempestuous lovers, Gwen and Aaron Mather. Her mouth firmed determinedly. She was going to have

14

to play this little scene very carefully. Amanda would never forgive her if it got out of hand.

Lang didn't look back as he climbed the stairs, providing Kali a moment to absorb the impact of him dressed in elegant black and white evening clothes. He radiated the intensity of a man on his way to a potentially violent confrontation.

A victim of his own passions, Kali thought in wry amusement. She gave a small, mildly disgusted shake of her neat head and moved softly across the beautifully carpeted foyer. It was amazing, she thought; the man on the stairs could easily have stepped out of the past, a hot-blooded Regency nobleman or a swashbuckling highwayman from an earlier generation. Perhaps a dangerous Renaissance swordsman or an eighteenth-century buccaneer, she mused, wondering at her own fantasies.

Whatever the origin of the illusion he projected, the basic message was clear: Lang Sterling was determined to regain possession of the woman with whom he'd arrived that evening. Kali's mouth quirked. Would he try calling out Aaron Mather? Did Lang even realize who the other man was? Probably not. Gwen was playing one of her little games and Lang, like it or not, had had the bad luck to become a pawn. Bad luck for him; potentially good luck for herself, Kali decided. Her gaze moved assessingly over her intended quarry.

Lang wore the sleek evening clothes well, his six feet of hard leanness defining its own style. The ruffled white shirtfront appeared abruptly masculine against the brown column of his throat. The deep russet hair was rakishly brushed into a thick, slightly long style that almost touched his collar in back.

Kali had gotten close enough once earlier in the evening to catch a glimpse of the bronze-green eyes which were shielded by unexpectedly heavy lashes. They had glittered with an awareness that bespoke the underlying intelligence. But, she reminded herself as she swept to the bottom of the staircase, she already knew the man was bright, at least in one rather limited area. It was the reason for her skillful pursuit.

The near-green eyes were the focal point of an utterly male, uncompromisingly unhandsome face. Fierce, craggy planes of jaw, nose, and cheekbone gave credence to Kali's wry imaginings. Lang Sterling didn't look like a man of the later quarter of the twentieth century. Eyeing him narrowly, Kali had to remind herself that he was going to make his fortune in a most futuristic fashion. The patents Lang held were, after all, in the field of robotics.

He was thirty-five years old and there was no doubt that in his area of expertise Lang was a highly refined, intuitive thinker, a man who had proven the power of his own intellect beyond a shadow of a doubt. It was too bad, Kali reflected, that outside his single field of accomplishment his mental and emotional development appeared to be throwbacks to a much different era. Judging from his current mood of aggression, she prayed it wasn't any more primitive an era than, say, the Stone Age.

Lang was at the first landing now. When he turned to follow the angled staircase the light from the sparkling chandelier fixture overhead caught the sharp, hard lines of his face and illuminated the deep fire buried in his hair. He didn't even notice Kali standing at the foot of the stairs, his whole, grim attention focused on what awaited him at the top.

Kali drew a breath. Now was the time to make her move.

"Forget her, Mr. Sterling, the game isn't worth the candle. Gwen Mather is still in love with her ex-husband. She was only using you this evening to goad him."

The man on the staircase froze at the sound of Kali's

16

cool, half-amused words. He stopped, one foot on the next tread, and looked down at the woman he hadn't noticed until that moment. The bronze-green eyes slitted with sudden speculation.

"Who are you?" His voice was dark, faintly and appealingly gritty. It also carried overtones of his obviously aggressive mood.

"The woman who's going to help make you rich," Kali smiled, unaffected by the intensity in him.

The green eyes narrowed a little further. She had his full attention. Slowly, with a care that told its own story, Lang turned to lean against the heavy oak railing of the staircase. He peered down at her reflectively.

"There are," he finally announced, "several people who are going to want to make me rich. You'll have to get in line."

"I am in line. I'm at the head of it."

He considered that for a moment. "You may have a point. But it doesn't matter tonight. I have other things on my agenda this evening besides business, you see," he explained almost cordially.

"Such as causing a major scene in the home of your hostess?" One eyebrow arched above the rounded frames of Kali's glasses. She waited for his answer, her hand resting lightly on the newel.

To her surprise he appeared to give her question serious thought. Finally he shook his head decisively. "I'm not causing the scene. I'm reacting to a situation which has been created by someone else and which may, indirectly, cause a scene."

"You shouldn't try to get involved in a discussion of semantics tonight," Kali suggested gently, "you've had a little too much to drink."

He smiled at that and Kali almost gritted her teeth at having provoked the sudden, savage slash of masculine

17

amusement. It wasn't the reaction for which she had been aiming. It was going to take all her skills to manipulate this man, she acknowledged.

"I may be a little too far gone to handle straight logic this evening," he conceded in a dark growl, "but I can still handle a woman. A fact Gwen Mather is about to discover."

"The only man Gwen is interested in is her husband, Aaron. He's the man who just preceded you up the stairs, by the way," Kali said hurriedly.

"Her husband!" Lang's features hardened.

"Well, her ex-husband," Kali admitted. "But anyone who knows either of them can tell you they'll undoubtedly be remarrying soon. They can't leave each other alone. The only reason Gwen's here tonight is because she found out Aaron would be here." Kali saw no reason at this delicate stage to explain that she had made certain Gwen knew her ex-husband would be attending Amanda's party. Nor was there any need to explain that she had known Lang was Gwen's latest conquest and therefore almost certain to be the male the other woman would bring to the affair.

"You're implying I was used this evening?" he drawled dangerously.

Kali winced inwardly. Wrong approach. If she pushed that angle he would only feel more obliged than ever to finish his ascent of the staircase. His ego would be irrevocably at stake.

"They're in love, Mr. Sterling. The relationship has been a bit rocky, but it's a strong one. If you climb those stairs you might possibly achieve a variety of macho objectives but none of them will make Gwen want to spend the night with you and all of them will cause a great deal of trouble to some innocent people."

18

"You're very concerned about how I spend my evening," he observed a little too blandly.

"Amanda Bryant is a friend of mine. She's worked very hard to make this reception a success for her husband. His career is involved tonight. You have the power to turn this party into a front-page embarrassment for him. Do you really want to do that?"

Lang frowned, leaning forward slightly to study her upturned face. "Gwen," he declared carefully, "is supposed to be helping me celebrate tonight. I shall merely go up the stairs, fetch her, and leave. If you keep people from coming out into the hall, there will be no one to see my grand exit," he added helpfully.

"Don't be ridiculous. Gwen's not about to leave quietly and her ex-husband is very likely to assist your grand exit by throwing you down the stairs!"

The bronze-green eyes glittered with promise. "Why don't you wait right there and see who comes down these stairs and in what condition!"

"It will be you first because Aaron hasn't been drinking as much as you have," Kali said coolly. This was a bit risky but the goal was to shift his attention from Aaron and Gwen to herself. Prodding him might be a way to do that.

Lang looked at her as if trying to decide how to deal with this unexpected and puzzling intrusion into his evening. "You've been counting my drinks?"

"Scotch on the rocks with a twist. Several of them," Kali murmured pleasantly.

"I'll be damned," he whistled soundlessly. "You've been spying on me."

"I like to know something about people before I offer them great sums of money," she retorted smoothly. Her copper-colored nails moved with unconscious anticipation on the top of the newel. He was definitely changing the

19

focus of his attention. All she had to do was keep playing him properly and he would be putty in her hands.

"What else do you know about me?" he demanded softly.

"Come down those stairs and drive me home. I'll tell you," she suggested coolly.

It was his turn to arch a dark russet brow. "You're offering to take Gwen's place for the evening?" he shot back easily.

"Not quite," Kali smiled, unperturbed. "I want to talk business with you this evening. There will be plenty of other women who will be happy to help you, uh, celebrate. My only interest is in seeing that you celebrate the right deal."

"A deal with you. Who the hell are you?"

"My name is Kali Havelock. I represent Interactive Automation, Inc." She stated the facts with calm assurance.

"IAI picked you to seduce me?" he muttered in evident disbelief. "Someone must have been crazy. A little research would have turned up the fact that I like blondes!"

Kali refused to rise to the obvious bait. He was deliberately trying to provoke her and she knew it. The man might be a genius in robotics but she was the one who knew all about handling people.

"I'm a vice-president at IAI, not a hired prostitute. I wish to discuss business with you, not seduce you." She smiled brilliantly in the glow of the chandelier. "You needn't worry, Mr. Sterling, you're no more my type than I am yours. But I think you'll find what I have to say most interesting. When you've concluded your deal with IAI you'll be able to attract any number of Gwens. Even a few, perhaps, who won't be encumbered with ex-husbands."

"You *are* trying to seduce me!" he accused. "With money!"

"Business." Kali shrugged.

He grinned wickedly. "IAI will still be willing to do business with me tomorrow morning. There's no reason I can't finish what I started tonight. Give me a call tomorrow, Kali Havelock. Any woman who knows what I drink will have my phone number." He moved as if to continue on up the stairs. "Just make sure you don't phone too early in the morning," he added vengefully. "I intend to sleep late!"

"What?" she mocked quickly, momentarily worried she might have mismanaged him. "Sleeping in late with tonight's little scene on your conscience? You're a guest in Sam Bryant's home tonight, Lang Sterling. Doesn't his career mean anything at all to you?"

He halted once more, glaring down at her. "I told you, go stand in front of the door and no one will witness my departure!"

She shook her head. "There's going to be a hell of a scene and you know it. Do you really want her back? Or would any woman do tonight?"

That had been a shot in the dark but it had found its target. Kali hid a smile of satisfaction as Lang's strong hand gripped the railing. His gaze was narrowed and full of menace but she knew she had him back in hand again.

"Any woman might do, Miss Havelock," he grated, his temper clearly ruling his head. "But Gwen happens to be the one who's available."

"Do you want her, knowing she's in love with another man?" Kali taunted. "If any woman would do this evening, why not find another?"

"There is a small matter of pride involved here!" he snapped, infuriated.

"That's easily handled. Leave with me, instead. Believe me, it'll drive Gwen crazy wondering what happened to you. There will be plenty of people eager to inform her you

21

left with another woman. It will be her pride which will suffer, not yours."

He stared at her with baleful admiration. "You've got an answer for everything, don't you?"

"It's part of my job," she said lightly. "Come with me, Mr. Sterling. I can offer you an infinitely more rewarding evening than any you might have with Gwen Mather."

"Financially rewarding, you mean," he muttered. "It so happens I'm interested in other things tonight." But he was waiting, waiting to see what she would do next, and Kali had to repress a smile.

"I'm prepared to offer more than money for your patents, Lang Sterling."

"I'm listening," he drawled in mocking invitation. Both hands gripped the rail now as he looked down at her. The bronze-green eyes held leaping devils.

"People who suddenly become very rich acquire a great many problems along with the money," Kali pointed out delicately. "Chief among those problems is an institution known as the IRS. Have you given much thought to your forthcoming tax situation, Mr. Sterling? Interactive Automation can assist you. There are other things a man in your line of work would like that IAI can supply. . . ."

"A woman for tonight?" he asked with an ingenuousness induced by the Scotch.

"How about a totally equipped lab? The best research assistance? A regular stipend in addition to an outright sum for your patents? A guarantee by IAI that it will buy any future patents?"

"Fascinating," he murmured. "But I really don't feel like going to work tonight. Tonight I plan to spend in bed with a warm and willing . . ."

". . . woman," Kali completed, a twinge of genuine irritation beginning to seep into her voice. She masked it

22

immediately, offering a charming smile, instead. "Even if you get Gwen back, she'll hardly be willing."

"How about you, Miss Havelock? Would you be willing?"

"Are you that desperate, Mr. Sterling? Or do you think you could put aside thoughts of immediate gratification in exchange for an evening of business which will benefit you for the rest of your life?"

"Was that a hint of a blush I saw there, Miss Havelock?" he demanded, bending over the rail as if to get a better look.

"No, Mr. Sterling. Vice-presidents do not blush."

"Pity."

"If you don't watch out, Mr. Sterling, you are going to fall over that railing, in which event you will be quite useless to either Gwen Mather or IAI," Kali observed crisply.

He looked interested. "Do you think I'm that drunk?"

"I'd say it's a distinct possibility after all that Scotch!"

"You're something of a nag, do you realize that, Miss Havelock?"

"I apply the appropriate methods to any given situation, Mr. Sterling." She smiled serenely, sensing victory. "Take me home now and I give you my word not to nag further."

"It is a measure of the power of your nagging ability that I'm even tempted by that proposition!"

"Perhaps it is a vision of your successful future which is tempting you," she hazarded cheerfully.

"For some reason I'm finding it difficult to look beyond this evening," he sighed, still leaning a little precariously over the staircase banister.

"Try, Mr. Sterling. It will be worth it, I promise you. In any event, your immediate future is going to look quite

23

bleak if you decide to continue on your present course of action."

He closed his eyes briefly in an expression of anticipated pain. "I had a feeling you were going to say something like that."

"Consider the fact, Mr. Sterling, that anyone involved in a scene such as the one you're about to precipitate will come out of the mess looking very foolish. It isn't only your host's career which might suffer. It isn't only your hostess who will be mortified. You are going to come off appearing like an overly macho idiot no matter how many heads you bash or how many women you carry off into the night. I am offering you a neat, efficient way out of the situation; one that will enable you to keep your pride intact and one that will start you on the road to a wealthy, established future. Furthermore, Amanda Bryant will be forever grateful for your self-control. She's well aware of the provocation you've had tonight. Her gratitude will rub off on her husband, of course, and there's no telling where Sam Bryant may end up in politics."

Lang shook his head a little dazedly. "Is that it for the Prosecution? Are you resting your case?"

"Only if I've presented enough evidence to convince you to come back down those stairs."

He drew a long breath, his eyes never leaving her composed face. "I trust, Miss Havelock, that IAI pays its vice-presidents very well?"

"IAI always pays well for talent," Kali assured him meaningfully.

"I wonder how many companies have need of people who can successfully talk drunken roboticists down from stairways," he mused, straightening.

"Have I accomplished that feat?" Kali inquired politely, trying to analyze his state of mind. He was definitely

24

at some inner turning point, although he still didn't move on the stairs.

"I believe you have, Miss Havelock," he allowed, starting slowly and deliberately back down. "For some strange reason you're beginning to fascinate me. Rather like a snake fascinates a rabbit."

"Are you saying I've hypnotized you, Mr. Sterling?" Kali hid her cool moment of triumph very well. She had, after all, been expecting success. Still, when she withdrew her fingertips from the top of the newel she was aware of how much tension there had been in her light grip on the post.

"Perhaps," he agreed with a mocking, narrow-eyed sadness. "It's not nice to go around taking advantage of drunken macho idiots, Miss Havelock." He halted on the step above her, one hand on the railing. "Tell me something: Am I going to hate myself in the morning?"

Kali smiled benignly up into the craggy face. "You're going to congratulate yourself in the morning, Mr. Sterling. Trust me."

"I think," he declared quite forcefully, "that I would be a fool to trust you. Look how easily you've just manipulated me."

"No, Mr. Sterling," Kali denied gently. "I only outlined the options involved. You chose the best one."

"We'll soon find out, won't we?" he retorted with a sudden, flashing grin. He took her arm in a surprisingly firm grip and started her toward the front door. "Let's go, Madame Vice-President. My future, or at least the remainder of the evening, awaits."

Kali cast a quick glance back toward the double doors, wondering if she should notify Amanda that all was safe.

"She'll figure it out for herself when there's no major scene conducted on the stairway," Lang murmured as if he'd read her mind. Kali lifted one velvet-clad shoulder in casual dismissal and allowed herself to be led outside into the cold chill of a Seattle winter's night.

"Did you bring a car tonight?" she asked calmly, scanning the narrow street in front of the Bryants' home. The exclusive section of Queen Anne Hill was jammed with exotic and luxurious cars.

"Took a taxi," Lang informed her succinctly.

"My car's over there," Kali said, her black velvet skirt sweeping around her ankles as she stepped forward.

He held out a hand with automatic demand. She glanced down at it and back up into his set face. "Yes?"

"The keys," he explained impatiently.

"I'll drive."

He slanted a dark look down at her as they walked briskly toward the waiting silver Porsche. "Who, may I ask, is taking who home?"

"You've had too much Scotch to drive," Kali pointed out coolly, removing the car keys from her small black-and-gold clutch.

"Which means you intend taking me home." He nodded resignedly. He slid into the passenger seat as she unlocked the door. "Which home?" he added hopefully.

"Mine, of course," Kali replied unconcernedly, starting the powerful, well-behaved engine with casual expertise. "I'm going to make a pot of coffee and we will have a nice talk about all that nice money you're going to get from IAI."

"I can't wait," he growled dryly. "For God's sake, look out. You nearly sideswiped that Mercedes!"

She glanced briefly at the car which had been parked ahead of her own. "There was plenty of room. Are you one of those men who gets nervous when a woman is driving?"

"Not generally, but I freely admit there is something about you, Miss Havelock, which is beginning to terrify me!" She was aware of his wary gaze on her calm profile

26

as she negotiated the winding streets down from Queen Anne Hill. Ahead of them the lights of downtown Seattle gleamed, the towering Space Needle a jeweled ornament in the night sky.

"Relax, Mr. Sterling. You made a wise decision tonight. You won't regret a thing."

"May I remind you that the only thing I've agreed to so far is to take you home and already you've manipulated that to the point where it's *you* taking *me* home?" he complained coldly.

Kali laughed, unable to keep the edge of satisfaction out of her voice. "Believe me, tomorrow morning you're going to be grateful to me when you wake up and realize that not only did I save you from making a fool of yourself but I've also presented you with a business proposition which will ensure your financial well-being for the rest of your life."

She shot him a quick glance when he didn't respond immediately. The thick, dark lashes came down to veil the bronze-green eyes as he sat watching her.

"I'm still having trouble ignoring the fact that you've ruined my evening, Miss Havelock. I suppose it's all that Scotch I've consumed, but I find myself overly preoccupied with the thought of having been denied the feminine companionship I'd planned on enjoying. Have you any suggestions on how I should deal with that little problem, Madame Vice-President?"

Something flickered awake in Kali at the thread of danger entangled deep in his drawling, gritty voice. It was something ancient and unbearably primitive, an instinctive, feminine caution which heretofore had been quite unknown to her.

"Surely a discussion of your long-range future takes precedence over the disappointment of a somewhat blighted evening, Mr. Sterling," she admonished with a casual-

27

ness she didn't altogether feel. Unconsciously her copper-tinted nails curled a little more tightly around the steering wheel.

"I'm not sure about that, Miss Havelock," he retorted evenly. "I'm not at all sure about that. Some men could channel a certain amount of masculine frustration into a business discussion; some men could not. It will be interesting to find out which category I fall into, won't it?"

CHAPTER TWO

"Hell of a view!" was Lang's first comment as Kali opened the door to her high-rise condominium apartment. It was one of the few totally sincere remarks he had made during the drive back downtown, she decided ruefully.

He shoved his hands into the front pockets of his black dress slacks and ambled across the darkened living room toward the glass wall which provided a stunning view of Elliott Bay and the Seattle waterfront. The lights of a ferry shone brightly against the dark mass of water as it plied its way on a commuter run between the scattering of islands on Puget Sound.

"You'll be able to afford an even better one when you collect all that money IAI is going to pay you for your patents," Kali began bracingly as she slipped off her velvet jacket and dropped it absently over the back of a nearby chair.

The view seemed to hold his entire attention for a long moment as he considered that. Kali doubted if he'd even noticed the rest of the apartment. And it was true, the view did tend to dominate, she thought with an inner smile. But she was satisfied with the remainder of the decor, too. A plush, chocolate-brown carpet swept from wall to wall, providing a deep contrast for the well-designed, luxuriously modern furniture. The low, styled modular sofa was in a rich shade of yellow, as was the chair across from it. A square, glass-topped coffee table separated the two.

White walls hung with a variety of modern prints framed the room and the remainder of its yellow, white, and glass furniture. Three low steps led up to the elevated dining area where an unusual Italian brass-and-glass jigsaw dining table occupied center stage. The entire apartment reflected Kali's life-style quite well. It was modern, well-designed, and functional. And it had an air of quiet opulence underlying all.

It was as she was walking into the kitchen to start the coffee that Lang finally responded to her comment about his being able to afford a spectacular view. It wasn't the sort of remark she had been expecting but, given his mood, she probably should have.

"Do you always talk business with the men you bring back to your apartment?" he asked with a cool, rasping insolence that Kali knew she would do well to ignore.

She glanced through the opening provided in the wooden cupboards which separated the kitchen from the living area, frowning slightly as she studied his straight back. His dark head was bent as he gazed, seemingly fascinated, at something on the street below.

"Frequently," she murmured dryly.

He turned at that, pacing moodily across the rich brown carpet to come to a halt in the kitchen doorway. Lounging against the jamb, one hand still thrust into a pocket, he watched her make the coffee, the bronze-green eyes shadowed beneath the heavy lashes. Kali was well aware of the fact that he didn't quite know what to make of her. It was one of the reasons she'd been able to manage him so easily thus far.

"What a thrilling life you must lead," he observed testily.

"It suits me." She smiled, her smoky eyes mirroring her inner amusement. "Cream or sugar?" Her hand poised, ready to remove the glass pot from the automatic coffee maker.

"Scotch. With a twist. Remember?"

"I'm serving coffee," she told him calmly. "You've had enough Scotch. I wouldn't want you agreeing to something tonight and then reneging in the morning on the grounds that you couldn't remember!"

"I'm really not in a mood to discuss business tonight," he announced casually, accepting the white mug she more or less forced into his hand. He looked down at the dark liquid as if it were poison. "I'd rather have Scotch."

"Come, Mr. Sterling, let's go into the living room and talk about your brilliant future with IAI," Kali said briskly, leading the way. She could feel him glaring at the gold stripe in the black silk which covered her slender back, but he reluctantly pried himself away from the wall and followed. Once more Kali was forced to conceal a smile.

"Have a seat, Mr. Sterling . . ."

"Lang," he muttered, setting his mug on the glass table and flinging himself in a coordinated sprawl into the corner of her yellow sofa. "Call me Lang. It seems appropriate under the circumstances . . . I mean, having kidnapped me and all . . ."

"Thank you, Lang," Kali said formally, ignoring the little barb. "I'm Kali."

"Vice-president Kali," he clarified.

"About your patent package, Lang," she began smoothly. "I'd like to spell out exactly what IAI is prepared to pay, both in terms of dollars and fringe benefits . . ."

31

"What I really want to know at the moment," he interrupted, eyeing the polished toe of his shoe as he stretched one leg along the sofa cushions, "is how much IAI is prepared to compensate me for having ruined my birthday."

Behind the crisp, bold frames of her glasses, Kali blinked. He'd finally succeeded in putting her slightly off stride, she acknowledged privately. "Your birthday!"

He looked up, smiling a bit loftily. "My birthday. Tonight I was celebrating my birthday when you chose to interfere in my life. I'm thirty-six," he added kindly.

"I see. Well, congratulations," she managed and then pressed on with cheerful enthusiasm. "What better time to discuss your future, then, hmmm?"

Lang's smile disappeared and he regarded her evilly. "Has anyone ever seriously discussed *your* future with you? Your *immediate* future?"

Sensing she'd pushed too far, Kali instantly retreated behind a soothing smile and took a sip of coffee while she frantically reassessed the amount of pressure which could be applied. "As a matter of interest, Lang, I'd like to point out that my future, well-established as it is, will look even better if you agree to sell your robot sensor patents to IAI."

"Ah-hah! I'm to be a nice little coup for you, is that it?" he pounced, leaning farther back into the corner of the couch and lacing his fingers across his chest.

She decided to ignore that. "How familiar are you with IAI's work in the field of industrial robots?"

"Familiar enough to contact your management after I patented the new vision and touch sensors," he shot back.

"How many companies did you contact?" Kali tried to keep the question light and bland. Mentally she was going through a list of probable competitors.

"About five," he told her easily. "Of the five I figured two would be sufficiently interested to put in a bid."

"IAI and who else?" Kali tried to will away the cool sizzle of tension which had started through her nervous system.

"I'm expecting great things from Hadley Industrial Systems." He smiled deliberately, watching her closely to see how she took the news of competition. "Ever hear of them?"

Kali's copper nails tightened around her mug but the cool smile on her lips never faltered. *Hadley!* He'd contacted Hadley Industrial Systems. If he only knew just how much she had heard of the other company!

"A small, growing firm out of Palo Alto, California, isn't it?" she replied.

"Which will undoubtedly be willing to pay a fortune to get a jump on the market with my new sensors." Lang appeared quite pleased with himself.

"IAI will be quite willing to compete," she assured him. "My firm is determined to bring out the next generation of industrial robot. As you know the Japanese will soon be dominating the market if American industry doesn't get moving."

It was a combination of the development of the microprocessor in the mid-sixties and a need for increased productivity which had brought about the budding robot revolution in the industrialized workplaces of the world. The modern robot was not a futuristic monster as first envisioned in Mary Shelley's story of Dr. Frankenstein, nor had it evolved as a mechanized creature of either good or evil as more contemporary science-fiction authors had fantasized.

The industrial robot of the 1980s was basically a skilled, manipulating machine capable of welding and painting automobiles, transporting radioactive materials behind shielded walls, and sampling the mysteries of outer space in such adventures as the trip of *Voyager 1*.

Robots could currently be designed to resemble something from a science fiction novel, complete with mobility and an ability to speak English. But from a practical standpoint it was cheaper and more efficient to anchor them to an assembly line and plug them into a computer.

One of the factors currently limiting the type of work modern robots could perform was the limitation of sensory systems. A television camera was not an adequate substitute for a more sophisticated vision system and a claw which could measure size was not a very viable alternative to the sense of touch.

Lang Sterling's contribution to the field of industrial robotics was a brilliant new concept for providing a programmable machine with far more advanced sensory systems than currently existed. The company which bought the rights to his patents would have a tremendous jump on the market.

It was a continuing source of amazement to Kali that the man who could have designed such technology could spend the nonbusiness side of his life thinking and acting in a manner which would have embarrassed any robot. How could a man with the ability to think so logically get drunk on his birthday and threaten a scene which would have been appropriate to the behavior of a gentleman from two or three hundred years in the past?

And why did that man insist on giving more attention to his ruined birthday celebration than to a discussion of the financial rewards he was going to earn as a result of his work?

"We both know I'm going to be rich," Lang drawled complacently. "But I don't see any need to go into the details tonight. It *is* my birthday, after all. I really don't care about foreign robot competition this evening."

Kali tried a new tack. "One would think, judging from the way you've been living lately, that you already were rich . . ."

"The marvels of a credit card society," he returned blandly. "By the time the bills come due I will have collected for my patents. You don't have to worry about me going into bankruptcy. Kind of you to be concerned, of course, but totally unnecessary. Just how much spying have you done on me?"

"I made it my business to find out something about you before I approached you." She shrugged with a wry twist to her lips. It was the truth. She didn't believe in going into any venture unprepared. "I wanted to have a good shot at convincing you IAI could give you whatever you desired, within reason. It was necessary to learn a little about you."

"All that work and you didn't even learn that today was my birthday!"

Kali drew rein on her patience. "A slight oversight."

"Perhaps as a birthday present and as a way of making up for your oversight, you could fix me some Scotch on the rocks?" Lang favored her with a dazzling, alarmingly persuasive smile.

She thought about it, sipping her coffee with a slightly furrowed brow. "If I get you the Scotch would you settle down and talk business?"

"Trying to bribe me?" he demanded interestedly.

"I suppose so."

He made a clucking sound, shaking his head. "To what depths will IAI sink in order to get their greedy little hands on my patents?"

Kali set down her mug and got determinedly to her feet. "I'll get you another glass of Scotch, but in return I expect a little cooperation, Lang."

He watched her over the tip of his shoe as she moved

across the living room to a sleek white and chrome liquor cabinet. "Don't forget the twist."

"I don't have any lemon. You'll have to drink it plain." She poured the drink grudgingly and came gliding back to the couch, her expensively booted feet making no sound on the carpet. Standing beside his sprawled form on the couch, she handed him the glass.

"Scotch wasn't the only thing you deprived me of this evening," he reminded her, reaching up to close his hand around the glass.

Kali's eyes narrowed at the male speculation she caught behind his lashes. "No," she agreed bluntly, "I also deprived you of the opportunity of making a fool out of yourself. Under the circumstances, you ought to be grateful to me, Lang!"

Before she could remove her fingers from the glass he was in the process of taking from her hand, Lang moved, reaching up to close his other hand around her wrist in a grip of casual strength. The bronze-green eyes fairly glittered at her small gasp of surprise.

"Allow me to show you just how grateful I am, Vice-President Kali Havelock," he grated with such unexpected vehemence that Kali was startled. She thought she'd been managing him quite well but she hadn't guessed just how close to a boil his temper had been simmering.

Now she had a very clear, very dramatic glimpse of it as he put the glass of Scotch on the table with great care and tugged her down onto his lap.

"Lang! What do you think you're doing? Let go of me, damn it, you're drunk!"

Her initial, totally automatic reaction was to struggle and unthinkingly Kali did so for a few angry, startled moments. It was not the right way to handle the situation, she realized almost at once. Catching both her wrists in one manacle of a hand, Lang shifted. Somehow her body floundered down alongside his, trapped between his hard frame and the back of the couch.

"Stop squirming," he soothed in a gentling tone that threatened to make Kali's usually docile temper explode.

"Let me up, Lang! You don't know what you're doing!"

"I'm doing what I had planned to do on my birthday," he contradicted, stilling her kicking legs with a heavy thigh across the flowing black velvet of her long skirts. "I'll admit you're not the woman I had planned on doing it with, but a man has to be adaptable in this world . . ."

He brought his mouth down to hers with lazy, almost curious hunger, using the weight of his body and the grip on her wrists to hold her helplessly crushed into the cushions. Angrily Kali turned her head aside but he followed relentlessly, finding her mouth with his own.

The kiss was startlingly warm, tasting faintly of Scotch. He didn't rush the intimacy, letting his mouth cling lingeringly to hers as if giving Kali a chance to accept the contact. He made no immediate move to deepen the kiss by thrusting his tongue beyond the rigidly locked barrier of her small, white teeth.

With his free hand, Lang ran questing fingers down the length of her side to where the black velvet covered her hip. He was waiting expectantly and it took Kali a long moment to come to her senses and analyze exactly what it was he was waiting for.

Belatedly the rational part of her mind surged to the fore with typical businesslike efficiency. Lang was, of course, simply waiting to see what form her struggles would take. No doubt his frustration and annoyance over the matter of her interference with his evening needed to vent itself.

Kali had a mental image of the control he'd had to exert over his racing adrenaline when she'd talked him out of following Gwen and Aaron Mather upstairs. Add to that a certain amount of damaged male pride, too much Scotch, and an illogical, somewhat primitive nature and you had a definite time bomb on your hands.

He *wanted* a fight from her, she realized grimly. He wanted a chance to exert some control over an evening which had been radically disrupted. It was an understandable, if not particularly commendable, phenomenon. Desperately Kali racked her brains for the best way to handle matters even as the hand on her hip clenched goadingly.

"Wish me happy birthday, Vice-President Kali," he growled against her mouth. "Or throw in a little something extra with the Scotch. I'm open to bribery, I think. I haven't really encountered the genuine, blatant sort before but I'm willing to experiment . . ."

He lifted his head for a moment, regarding her with deliberate provocation. Kali drew in her breath, still trying to decide on the best means of manipulating the awkward situation. When he removed her glasses with a slightly menacing, taunting manner and put them behind him on the coffee table she reached a decision.

Lang Sterling was spoiling for a fight. He needed to mend some of the lacerated machismo she'd whittled on during the evening. He needed to work out some of his frustration and annoyance. Giving him the struggle he wanted and letting him, in essence, think he had *conquered* her on some level was probably the most efficient way of getting him back to a normal plateau. If Sterling could be said to have a normal, reasoning mode of operation!

"Come on, little Vice-President," he urged tersely, beginning to nuzzle her ear, "wish me happy birthday. Give me a kiss for a present . . ."

"I could care less about your birthday," she gritted, loosening one booted foot sufficiently to kick his shin. "I brought you here tonight to talk business! Let me go, Lang!"

The reward for her rebellion was a stinging nip on her earlobe which made Kali flinch. She had no reason to think Lang would become dangerously violent. There was nothing in the information she'd turned up on him to indicate real menace but he *had* consumed a fair amount of Scotch tonight . . . !

Nevertheless, her decision made, Kali proceeded to wage a furious struggle. She tried to push at him with her captured wrists, attempted a few more swipes at his vulnerable shins with her feet, and twisted her head from side to side in an effort to avoid his mouth. It was an amazingly realistic performance, she thought vaguely at one point, considering that was all it was.

"I wanted a woman in my bed tonight, Kali Havelock," he rasped huskily as she began to pant a little from her efforts. "Since you were so eager to substitute yourself for the one I had found on my own, you can damn well act the part!"

Still holding her wrists, he heaved himself upward far enough to tear off his elegant black evening jacket, dropping it in a heap on the carpet. Kali's eyes widened as he came back down beside her. Somehow, in that white, ruffled shirt, the black tie undone and hanging loose around her neck, his hair rakishly tousled, Lang Sterling was beginning to seem more of a difficult proposition to handle than she'd bargained for.

But she was committed to a course of action now. She would have to trust her instincts and abilities.

"I'm not about to let you manhandle me," she hissed.

"No?" He traced a path upward from the edge of the velvet skirt waistband, his fingers sliding over the silky lamé material of her blouse until they rested just beneath the curving weight of her small breasts.

"No!" But Kali's breath came with sudden sharpness as he touched her with an almost delicate caress.

"I should have known you were the type to wear a bra, even under a blouse and that jacket and even though you're only big enough to fill a man's hand . . . !"

"Sorry if I fail to please! You can leave your suggestions and comments behind on the appropriate form when you leave!" There were sparks behind the smoke of her eyes as she glared at him.

"I wasn't complaining," he retorted mockingly, letting his thumb probe for the nipple hidden beneath the layers of fabric. He touched his lips to her throat as she tried to arch her head back out of reach. "You feel just right in my arms."

In spite of herself Kali blinked at the tone of surprised wonder in his words. Who the hell did he think he was? With a rush of growing annoyance she writhed furiously beneath his hand. As she did so, his ear came within reach and she clamped at it aggressively with her teeth.

"Ouch!"

With another muttered word or two, Lang lifted himself, slid her abruptly beneath the full length of his body and came down on top of her in a heavy surge of hard, muscled weight. The impact took away her breath and Kali opened her mouth, automatically sucking in air.

She got his tongue instead. He took her lips with the swooping, stunning blow of a hawk, thrusting into the depths behind her teeth before she could gather her senses.

But her hands were free at last! Kali splayed her fingers against his shoulders, shoving with all her strength. She might as well have been trying to lift a mountain. When that failed she tried to use her teeth against his invading tongue.

He retaliated by withdrawing far enough to take a warning nip out of her lower lip. Simultaneously his hands slid down her sides to her thighs, fingers flexing as they sought the feel of her beneath the tangled velvet.

When she gave up the attack on his tongue and allowed him to retake the interior of her mouth she knew he sensed an impending victory. Instead of softening the assault, however, he moved to consolidate his gains, using his knee to pry apart her legs. When she was forced to give ground once more he followed that up with a surging, fiercely intimate movement of his lower body against hers.

The action brought another gasp from Kali as she was made violently aware of the full force of his arousal. Wasn't heavy drinking supposed to deprive a man of his sexual abilities? How much Scotch had Lang consumed that evening? She'd been counting glasses at Amanda's party and she could have sworn . . .

Her efforts at logic were interrupted as she realized with a sense of widening shock that Lang's hand had discovered the fragile fastenings of the silk blouse. She was helpless to halt the progress of his hand and that fact finally drove her to acknowledge that it was time for the next stage of her battle plan. More than time! The battle had become real.

"Oh! Lang, please! I . . ."

The little cry was not entirely an act. Kali stopped fighting him, letting her body go soft and more acquiescent beneath his hardness. She couldn't have said in that moment what was buried in her small plea. Whatever it was, the important thing was that Lang should perceive it as a cry of surrender.

"Please what, Kali?" he prodded mockingly. But the assault was slowing as he accepted her implicit capitulation. Unfortunately the hand at work on the blouse fastenings didn't halt. Kali wasn't certain how to protest the intimacy without ruining the overall look of placating surrender.

41

"I'm . . . I'm sorry I provoked you," she got out faintly, closing her eyes as he reached the barrier of her bra and found the front clasp. No! He mustn't . . . !

But he was touching her, his thumb and forefinger finding the tip of her breast and the hardening bud of her nipple. She sensed the gathering tautness, felt a full sensation that was making her ache in a vulnerable, almost painful way.

And then, before she could find a way to stop him, Lang was trailing a string of fiery little kisses down her throat to the throbbing nipples, soothing them with the curling tip of his tongue.

"Oh!" The moan was half-stifled in her throat as he groaned huskily and tugged gently on one rosy peak. "Lang, no! I . . . Please, I don't . . ." But the protest was broken, terribly disjointed, and he ignored it. His whole attention seemed to be on eliciting a reaction from her body. With teasing dominance he licked concentric circles from the base of her breasts to the nipples and back again.

Kali realized she was straining upward against the weight of his body, unconsciously seeking more of him. Her fingers laced behind his head, burying themselves in the thick, dark red hair and pulling him closer.

What was wrong with her? She was in danger of losing control of the situation entirely, just when her plan seemed to be working! And it was working, she told herself frantically. The male aggression which had at last been satisfied when she had ceased fighting him had now transformed itself into a sensual, seeking quest for a different kind of satisfaction. Now was the time to retake the reins and guide him back into the path she wished him to pursue.

Kali did not fully understand why it should have taken such an act of willpower to begin the process of bringing Lang back into line. In that moment she didn't particularly want to dissect and analyze the matter. First things first.

"I'm sorry," she breathed again, forcing her fingertips to move in a soothing, massaging action through his hair to the nape of his neck. "I shouldn't have tried to push you tonight. It's only that I . . . I was so eager to talk to you . . ."

Reluctantly he lifted his head, moving his hands upward to cradle her face between slightly rough palms. The bronze-green eyes roved her anxious, wide-eyed expression with a warm, searching glance that held the flames of a surprisingly deep desire.

"We'll talk," he vowed. "Later."

Sensing the extremely precarious nature of the moment, Kali chose her words with the greatest care. "Lang, I hardly know you. You can't mean to carry this any . . . any further. I know . . ." she paused to touch the tip of her tongue to suddenly dry lips, "I know I've brought the situation on myself, but you must believe me, I never meant to make you angry."

He smiled with a slow, compelling sensuality that took her breath away. "I'm not angry. Not any longer."

"Then why . . . why are you continuing to punish me?" she asked very softly.

"Punish you! Is that what you call it?" The near-green eyes flickered with devilish laughter.

Instinctively Kali hid her expression behind the protection of her lashes. "Our . . . our relationship should be a business one . . ." she whispered.

"I've been telling you all evening I'm not particularly interested in doing business tonight," he growled, but she heard the soft note of masculine indulgence and had to work in order to stifle a sigh of relief. Things were back in hand. Only men who felt in control were inclined to be indulgent. Her tactics had worked.

"I realize that, but business is all I've had on my mind,"

she said with charming honesty. "You've taken me by surprise and I . . . I need time to recover. After all, I really don't know you *that* well!"

"We could know each other very well by morning," he murmured suggestively, bending his head slightly to feather a kiss along her jaw.

"It was Gwen you wanted tonight, not me," she pointed out with what she hoped was a proper degree of wistfulness.

"Ah." He nodded with complacent understanding. "So that's the problem. You don't like the idea of being a substitute, is that it?"

She bit her lip and hoped the gesture didn't come off as too ingenuous. "I'd rather know for certain that I'm wanted for myself, not because *any* woman would do or because I was being used in retaliation for what I swear was only an overeagerness to do business . . ."

He hesitated as if turning the problem over in his mind. "You're talking about pride, Kali Havelock," he finally told her with a hint of arrogance in the underlying indulgence. "My pride's suffered quite a bit at your hands this evening," he added by way of a reminder.

"I realize that now," she admitted humbly. What she was actually realizing, she told herself disgustedly, was that she hadn't handled him all that well this evening. Well, live and learn.

He hesitated a moment longer and then abruptly sat up. With a flashing grin he reached for the glass of Scotch and saluted her. "Here's to pride," he intoned and swallowed a healthy dose.

Seeing her chance, Kali sat up carefully, her fingers working quickly on the opened clothing. "And to your birthday," she put in lightly.

His eyes gleamed. "To my birthday."

She eyed the receding Scotch. "Perhaps some more hot coffee?" she tried, inching her way around him and off the couch until she was standing beside him. She felt as if she were trying to inch away from a panther.

"Why not?" he agreed cheerfully, leaning back into the sofa. A lock of russet hair fell forward over one eye and the wicked smile he gave her had a strange effect on her senses. Kali turned quickly away, scooping up the mugs of cold coffee and starting eagerly toward the kitchen.

She realized as she poured out fresh coffee that she wasn't all that certain now of his mood. He didn't seem angry or even very irritated any longer but she wasn't sure exactly what had replaced the earlier emotion. Perhaps if she could get enough coffee down him he really would settle down to business.

There was the distinct possibility, she added silently, that things had simply gotten too far out of hand tonight. She might be forced to pour him into a taxi and send him on home. She could always start the whole business over again in the morning from a different angle.

Yes, that might be the most practical suggestion, she decided. She didn't care for her own state of mind or the way her fingers were shaking as she poured coffee. All of her senses felt ruffled and on edge and her breath was coming in quick, uneven little gulps. Damn! What in the world was wrong with her? She must get complete control over herself before she would be able to deal with Lang.

Toying with the various options left open this evening and not finding any that seemed suitable, Kali picked up the white mugs and started back out into the living room.

Only to stop short when she realized Lang wasn't where she had left him.

For a moment a shaft of genuine fear went through her. Then she spotted the toe of one black leather shoe sticking

45

out over the yellow arm of the sofa. Tiptoeing forward, Kali peered down over the back of the piece of furniture.

Lang Sterling had passed out peacefully on the yellow cushions.

CHAPTER THREE

It was the commanding buzz of the intercom which woke
Kali from a sound sleep the next morning. Her lashes
flickered open and she lay for a moment staring at the
ceiling of her white-and-yellow bedroom. There was another disturbing noise intruding along with the intercom.
It was the muffled sound of her shower.

The realization of who it must be making use of the
facilities drew a rueful groan from her as she sat up and
tossed back the yellow-and-white-striped down comforter.
Her bare feet met the rich brown carpet and she ran a
hand through the tangle of her long hair as she stood up.
The intercom hissed once more.

"Damn! Who in the world . . . ?"

Reaching for a quilted, Renaissance-red robe and her
glasses, Kali made herself decent with a few more grum-
bles, ignoring her hair, and padded out into the living
room.

The only sign of her unplanned houseguest was the
black evening jacket hanging on the back of a chair. She

was staring at it somewhat grimly when the intercom demanded her attention.

"I'm coming," she muttered at the heedless, inanimate object and punched down the communication button. "Yes?"

"Kali?"

She took her finger off the button as if it had burned her. Even through the mechanical box she was quite certain she recognized that voice. Her pre-coffee haze began to clear under the impetus of having to think quickly and logically.

"This is Kali," she finally responded noncommittally.

"It's Davis, Kali. I'd like to see you this morning." The pleasant, masculine voice held the subtle familiarity of an old friend. Davis Wakefield had already made his decision on how to approach her, Kali thought, not without a certain admiration. "Old friends."

"Davis! I had no idea you were in town!" Coolly she shifted the innuendo from "old friend" to "old business acquaintance." Two could play at this game. "What can I do for you?" She found herself chewing on her lower lip.

There was the briefest of pauses on the other end as Davis Wakefield assessed the bright, businesslike note in her voice. Kali smiled to herself. She could almost see the handsome features composed into a slight frown. Along with that image came the memory of carefully styled, tawny brown hair and cool, give-nothing-away hazel eyes. Davis Wakefield was a man in control; a man who was going places. She'd learned a lot from him, Kali thought wryly. Had she learned enough?

"I think you can guess what brings me to Seattle," Davis murmured coolly. "IAI and Hadley Industrial seem to be on the trail of the same rabbit."

The "rabbit" suddenly burst forth into song in the shower. It was an off-key rendition of a current country-

and-western hit and it sounded as though Lang was trying to supply the twang of the guitar along with vocals. Kali doubted Davis could hear the noise but it was enough to interrupt her own thinking processes.

"I beg your pardon, Davis?" she stalled, trying to reason her way through the situation.

"Let me come on up, Kali," he purred gently. "It's been a long time. If nothing else, we should discuss our mutual interest, don't you think? And I could sure use a cup of coffee," he added with such a large measure of camaraderie Kali almost winced. It wasn't like Davis to overdo the chosen image. Or had she merely become that much more perceptive during the past year?

"It's awfully early, Davis . . ."

"You're telling me! My plane landed about an hour ago at Sea-Tac airport and I'm still looking for a cup of coffee! You always did make some of the best, honey. Besides, don't you think we ought to compare notes?"

Compare notes! Kali did a quick summing up of the situation. What were the odds that she could launch a total blitz attack and convince Davis he might as well take himself back to Palo Alto without the "rabbit" in his snare?

The twanging second verse of the western ballad filtered through the distant roar of the shower. Kali slid a speculative glance toward the hall which led to the bath. If Davis thought she had Lang Sterling all wrapped up and ready to deliver to IAI, would he give up the battle before it had even begun?

The unpredictable element in all this, of course, was Lang himself. How would he react if she tried to play out a domestic little scene with him in front of another man? Especially when he discovered the other man was also eager to hand over a great deal of money for his patents?

Then again, what did she have to lose? She probably

49

wouldn't succeed in rousting her competition but she might give him some cause for worry. After all, there weren't that many explanations for finding a man in a woman's apartment at this hour of the morning. It was bound at least to give Davis a start if he were to get the impression she was in the habit of spending the night with the quarry.

"All right, Davis, come on up. I'm in 1012. Turn right when you get off the elevator."

"Thanks, Kali. Can't wait to see you. Been a long time, hasn't it?"

"About a year," she agreed, not allowing anything but casual cheerfulness to show in her words.

She walked away from the intercom box, her eyes narrowed in concentration. The off-key song was still going on in the shower, Lang's deep, gritty voice actually rather well suited to the country-and-western style. She hoped he would stay in there until Davis made it to her front door. A man in her shower would add a nice touch to the scene. And when that man finally emerged and was introduced . . . ?

In the few minutes it took her visitor to ride the elevator up to the tenth floor, Kali managed to run a brush through her dark hair, opting to leave it loose. She peered into the mirror critically and decided it gave her a more casual, at-home look.

It was as she busied herself with making the coffee that Kali began having second thoughts about the hastily contrived situation. There were too many variables involved, she told herself darkly. How was Lang going to react? She was counting on his male ego to carry off the situation in her favor but what if he decided this morning that business was more important?

Damn! She shouldn't have invited Davis up to the apartment, she thought bleakly as the doorbell chimed.

The situation was too tricky, too full of risks. Or was it? What did she have to lose? she asked herself again as she went to answer the summons. Even if the plan didn't have any effect she was no worse off than before, was she?

Deliberately, Kali forced an expression of pleasant serenity as she opened the door to the attractive man in the hall.

"Hello, Davis. Won't you come in?" Politely she stood back, watching him a little curiously, in spite of herself. It had, after all, been a year . . .

The hazel eyes moved over her with something of the same curiosity as Davis stepped into the room. "Kali," he said simply. Then he reached out and cupped her chin in his hands, drawing her close for a charming kiss of greeting.

Kali froze and then hastily beat back the instinctive reaction, furious with herself for even the slightest evidence of disquiet. With a cool effort of will, she let her face be lifted for the kiss. When Davis's lips brushed hers she could pinpoint the exact second that he became aware of the sound of the shower. A tingle of satisfaction went through her.

Lang had ceased his song shortly before the doorbell chimed but he hadn't yet turned off the water. The roar of it finally impinged on Davis.

The handsome brow furrowed and the charming kiss was abruptly broken off. "You have company?"

"Yes, as a matter of fact, I do. But please have a seat, Davis. I'll get you a cup of coffee. You're looking well," she added lightly as she gestured him toward the yellow sofa. Belatedly she realized the black evening jacket still hung on the chair. Davis saw it almost at once but made no comment. She sensed an element of confusion in him, however, and gloried in it.

"You have a lovely apartment here, Kali," he began

51

with deceptive ease, strolling over to the huge windows. "When did you move from the place on Capitol Hill?"

"About six months ago."

An abrupt silence descended on the room as the shower was turned off. Kali slanted a subtle glance at Davis as she poured coffee. His lean frame in the dark business suit seemed to tense briefly.

"Is your, uh, visitor going to be upset finding me here?" he asked crisply, turning as she came into the living room with the mugs. The hazel eyes regarded her with a level, assessing glance.

"You mean is he going to beat you to a pulp? Have no fear, Davis," she chuckled, taking a seat. "My visitor is a business acquaintance." Her gray gaze held the essence of unconcerned blandness.

"Business?" He glanced pointedly at the black jacket as he sat down on the sofa.

"Why, yes. You of all people should know how easy it is to combine business with pleasure. You're the one who taught me the trick." She smiled politely. "And I've never forgotten the final lesson, you'll be happy to know. The business end of things must always predominate."

Davis reached for his coffee, eyes cool. Kali could almost feel him weighing her mood and deciding how to handle it. "Kali, you can't blame me for the way things turned out. Who could have foreseen the offer from Hadley at that particular time? And you certainly can't say the end result hasn't benefited your career!"

"Oh, it has," she drawled obligingly. "Enormously. But even though things have all turned out for the best, I find it's difficult to get over my annoyance at being *used.*"

He shrugged faintly beneath the expensive material of his jacket. "It was a matter of timing. One has to move when the opportunity is hot, after all."

"I couldn't agree more," she murmured, sipping her coffee.

She didn't know what she would have said next. The tense moment was shattered by a lighthearted whistling version of the country-and-western song which had begun in the shower. She glanced toward the hall, swallowing her sip of coffee with great caution.

Across from her Davis Wakefield stiffened. She could hear his teeth coming together in a near-silent gesture of irritation and his head turned as he followed her gaze.

With the nonchalance of a man intent on making himself perfectly at home, Lang Sterling sauntered into view, obviously en route to the kitchen. He was wearing one of Kali's huge chocolate towels wrapped around his waist and nothing else at all. The russet hair gleamed damply from the shower and droplets of water clung to the expanse of crisp reddish brown hair covering his chest.

Kali knew a moment of sensual shock which she frantically masked. Last night Lang had gotten no farther than removing his jacket and unknotting the formal tie. She had felt the smoothly muscled power in his body, sensed the bold contours of his maleness as he'd pinned her beneath him. But she hadn't really seen the sinewy line of his arm from elbow to wrist, nor had she been given an opportunity to visualize the tapering tangle of hair as it marched with rough, blatant masculinity down to his waist and beyond. The lean hips and strong thighs were aggressively evident beneath the towel and she found herself wondering fleetingly how he'd kept his tan well into the Seattle winter.

But the one thing she didn't have to concern herself with in that moment was the worry about how her moment of disconcerted reaction to Lang's near-nakedness was affecting either of the two men. They appeared totally oblivious to her presence as they confronted each other across the short expanse of carpet.

Even though Davis held the advantage of being somewhat prepared, it didn't seem to do him much good. He looked as taken aback as if he'd had no notion of the fact that there was a man in the apartment. He simply stared at Lang. For once, thought Kali with inner delight, the great Davis Wakefield didn't quite know how to handle a situation.

The problem didn't seem to bother Lang, however. After coming to a short halt during which he looked Davis up and down, he continued on into the kitchen. But he was clearly by no means indifferent to the discovery of another male visitor.

"Who the hell are you?"

The question was a hard growl of demand. Kali held her breath, hearing the small noises which told her Lang was pouring himself a cup of coffee. He emerged a moment later, mug in hand, and stood with his feet spread slightly apart, awaiting an answer. The bronze-green eyes were narrowed and glittered with belligerence. He ignored Kali completely, his whole attention on the other man.

From a store of resourcefulness which Kali had long since learned to respect, Davis recovered his aplomb.

"Davis Wakefield. I'm a friend of Kali's." He made no move to follow up the introduction with a proffered hand. Instead there was a deliberately laconic tone in his words designed to imply a relationship which was considerably more than friendly. Kali felt the tension uncurl in the pit of her stomach.

"Not any longer, you aren't." Lang's response was immediate and uncompromising. The gleaming gaze finally swung to Kali's carefully bland expression. "Say good-bye to your friend, sweetheart, and show the nice man the door."

54

He had a lot of nerve, she thought distractedly, challenging her to defy him like this. If it wasn't for the awkward fact that he was reacting exactly as she wanted him to react she would have taken the opportunity to put him in his place. As it was . . .

"Whatever you say, darling," she said quite meekly, looking at a thin-lipped Davis and wondering if he would go quietly.

"A business acquaintance, I believe you said," he gritted, getting to his feet.

"Oh, he is," she assured him, leading the way toward the door. He *was* going to go quietly. But, then, Davis hated scenes. He preferred to finesse a situation, not participate in a head-on encounter. He was also smart enough to back off when he knew he didn't have all the facts or answers.

But the hazel gaze was bright with suppressed anger as he paused at the door she was holding open. In a low-voiced whisper he muttered, "Where'd you pick up the Neanderthal? I wouldn't have guessed him to be your type!"

"Like I said," she retorted gently, aware of Lang in the kitchen doorway leaning against the jamb while he sipped hot coffee and watched Davis's departure, "it's business." And then, just as she urged him along by starting to shut the door, "His name's Lang Sterling. Otherwise known as the 'rabbit'!"

She closed the door firmly in Davis's startled face, locking it with a flick of her wrist and whirling to relax back against it in complete satisfaction. There was laughter in her smoky eyes and more amused triumph in the curve of her mouth as she faced a scowling Lang Sterling across the room.

Outside in the hallway she could hear the elevator re-

55

sponding to what had undoubtedly been an infuriated, frustrated command.

Lang absorbed the sight of her inner humor and the aura of satisfaction Kali knew she must be radiating. "That," he declared evenly, "is a nasty habit."

She looked at him in mild astonishment, her mind busy with the potential ramifications of the situation she had just manipulated. Coming away from the door she glided back toward her unfinished coffee.

"I beg your pardon?"

"I am referring to your habit of dragging men up to your apartment at all hours of the day and night. The least you could do is let one leave before you bring on the next in line!"

Something in his voice got through to her, a strong measure of male disgruntlement. "Lang . . ."

"Look," he interrupted bluntly, expression hardening, "I know I was a disappointment last night, passing out and all, but you didn't have to bring on a replacement this quickly!"

She stared at him over the rim of her cup. "Don't be ridiculous. I didn't go out looking for a replacement. Davis is an old acquaintance who happened to arrive in town on an early plane this morning. Quite natural that he should look me up."

"He's more than an old business acquaintance!"

Kali said nothing, contemplating his prickly mood. This was more than mere annoyance. Yet it couldn't possibly be jealousy. She rather thought Lang Sterling didn't like her very much to begin with so he could hardly be jealous. She had relied on his automatic, territorial instincts and the fact that he was the kind of male who would react first to the sort of situation she had established and think about it later. It had worked but if she wanted to strengthen her hand she had better guide matters carefully from here on in.

"His name is Davis Wakefield," she began, sitting down on the chair across from the sofa and regarding him smilingly.

"I got that much!" Irritably Lang came forward and took the sofa.

"You're going to get the cushions all wet," she pointed out politely. He sprang to his feet at once.

"Sorry," he rasped. "I'll get dressed so that we can continue this discussion without ruining your furniture!"

He slammed down the mug with undue violence and headed for the bath. By the time he reappeared wearing the lean, close-fitting slacks and the white ruffled shirt unbuttoned halfway down his chest, Kali had had time to sort out the various options. She tilted her head as he entered the living room, watching as he ran one of her combs through his thick russet hair with an impatient movement. She didn't want to admit that her real reason for forcing him back into his clothing was that the sight of him sitting in only a towel was much more disturbing than it should have been.

"So who is he, Kali?" Lang demanded forcefully, tossing down the comb and reaching once more for his coffee. He eyed her sharply.

"It's a long story," she hedged.

"I'm listening."

"Well, the part which would be of most interest to you is that he represents Hadley Industrial Systems," she announced casually.

Lang nearly choked on the coffee. "What?" he finally managed to splutter, looking stunned. "Hadley? He represents *Hadley?*"

"I'm afraid so." She smiled kindly. "The man you just

57

kicked out of my apartment is my chief competitor for your patents."

"Oh, my God," he whispered, appalled.

"Yes," she said simply. "An awkward situation for you."

"Oh, my God."

"More coffee?" she asked solicitously.

Lang disregarded the offer in favor of pinning her with a raking glance. "You set me up!"

"Absolutely not," she denied bracingly. "I had no idea Davis was going to show up here this morning. I didn't even know Hadley Industrial Systems was in the running until you mentioned it last night!"

"You can't deny it all worked out rather neatly for you!"

"I was an innocent bystander," she demurred. "Nobody asked you to make a fool of yourself by playing the heavy-handed lover scene."

"Last night," he flung back, rising tautly to his feet, "you were very concerned about saving me from playing that sort of scene." He made for the window, running a restless hand through his freshly combed hair. Then he swung around to confront her accusingly. "But last night it was in your favor to keep me from making a fool of myself, wasn't it? This morning it was to your advantage to let me try and start a fight with someone I had intended to cultivate! Talk about manipulative, industrial robots! You're worse than Nalg!"

"Nalg?" she inquired tersely, not liking his accusations.

"Forget it," he grated, beginning to pace tensely back and forth in front of the window. His stride was long and catlike, filled with his irritation. "Of all the conniving, manipulative, sneaky, underhanded . . . !"

"There was nothing sneaky or underhanded about my behavior!" Kali wasn't certain why she bothered with the

58

protest. He was obviously not in a mood to listen to her defense, but she felt compelled to say something on her own behalf. "I acted in a perfectly straightforward, businesslike fashion."

"*Businesslike!*" He glared at her as he turned and started back in front of the window. "Where the hell did you learn such *businesslike* behavior, Kali Havelock?"

She took a steadying breath. She would not let his accusations upset her. There was a job to do. "You just met the man who taught me everything I know."

That stopped him for an instant. "Wakefield? Who is he, anyway?"

"I've told you, he represents Hadley Industrial Systems. He's president and chief executive officer, in fact."

He moved a hand in a flat, dismissing arc, shaking his head shortly. "I mean, who is he to you? And don't feed me that pablum about his being an old business acquaintance!"

His restless tension was beginning to affect her, in spite of her determination to remain serenely in control. "But that's just exactly what he is!"

"Kali, so help me, I've stood about all I'm going to from you . . . !"

"You want all the gory details?" she charged, horrified at seeing her temper begin to slip. "Okay, I'll give them to you. Davis and I used to work together at IAI. I was one step below him on the corporate ladder and he taught me an incredible amount of useful techniques for manipulating a situation to the best possible advantage. He has an instinct for situations and people which had brought him one promotion after another and I was eager to learn everything I could. Then came the day he was tapped for a vice-presidency at IAI. But there was a catch! Upper management had heard he was something of a playboy and they wanted a man in the new position to be a little more circumspect. In short, they made it clear they would prefer a married man in the new vice-presidency post. IAI is a little old-fashioned in some respects," Kali broke off curtly.

"Go on," Lang prodded coldly.

"The next thing I knew the man I admired most in my business world was asking me to marry him!" She flung up her head, eyes sparkling angrily through the lenses of her glasses.

"You were engaged to Wakefield?" he demanded bluntly.

"For about one month."

"What happened?" Lang charged, hands on his hips as he paused once again in his restless pacing.

"Before the vice-presidency was finalized, another offer came through. Davis was asked to assume the presidency of Hadley Industrial Systems. Hadley," she went on, pulling her temper back under control with an effort, "is a much more progressive company than IAI, at least in terms of upper management! They didn't require that their new CEO be married."

"I'll be damned," Lang whispered in amazement. "So he broke off the engagement and went off to Palo Alto, is that it?"

"In a nutshell. Except for one last detail." Kali managed a bright little smile.

"Which is?"

"After Davis left for Palo Alto there was still a vice-presidency to be filled at IAI," she pointed out gently.

He regarded her grimly. "And you were the next most qualified candidate?"

"Yes."

"I see." He shook his head ruefully. "Your management didn't require that you, too, get married?" he demanded dryly.

"I didn't have Davis's somewhat reckless reputation," she retorted coolly. "Besides, they needed someone with his abilities and contacts. I was the next obvious person in line. If you can't get the master, you take the master's apprentice."

"Incredible," he bit out in mocking admiration. "And it's just my bad luck to be the pawn in your little scheme to, number one, prove to your management that you're every bit as good as the man they would have preferred and, number two, take a bit of revenge against said preferred male, is that it?"

The unexpected stab of insight was completely unwelcome and, Kali told herself furiously, completely off base. "That's not it at all! I'm merely out to do a job and I will do it to the best of my ability!"

"And your job is to snag me," he said, nodding.

"My firm is more than willing to pay well for you and your patents," she reminded him heatedly.

"You guessed I wanted to get both Hadley and Interactive Automation involved in a bidding war!" he accused.

"You don't need to involve us in a bidding war! We'll pay top dollar and we can offer a lot of other benefits besides money!"

"Last night, I take it, was an example?" he riposted with a sudden and very dangerous smile. He flicked a meaningful glance at the yellow sofa.

To her unbearable chagrin, Kali felt herself turn scarlet. Damn it! She would not let this . . . this *throwback* to another age embarrass her like this! Nevertheless she found herself on her feet, hands clenched at her side.

"No, Mr. Sterling, last night was not an example of what IAI is prepared to offer! You never gave me a chance to go into the details of our offer because you were disgustingly drunk and determined to make a fool out of yourself one way or another!"

"Not so drunk I can't remember how you felt lying under me on that sofa," he shot back brutally. "And not so drunk I don't remember the way you were beginning to respond. I recall very vividly, for example," he pursued ruthlessly, "how nicely your small breasts fit my hand, how hard and tight the nipples were when I kissed them, how your legs seemed to entwine with mine, how nicely your hips fit against mine . . ."

"Lang Sterling!" Her infuriated screech of protest was nearly blocked in her throat by the force of her emotion. What was she letting him do to her, for God's sake?

"I thought you told me last night that vice-presidents don't blush," he remarked in a completely altered tone of voice.

"How dare you?" she breathed, fighting valiantly for her self-control.

He regarded her with a smug blandness that made her want to strike him. "Dealing with robots is easy for me. I'm an expert on the subject, remember?"

"Of all the despicable, disgusting . . ."

"Come now," he retorted bracingly, moving toward the chair where his jacket hung. "That's no way to conduct a business discussion."

"Business discussion!"

He nodded, shrugging into the jacket. "We still have business to transact, you and I. I suggest tomorrow night. Dinner at my place. Agreeable? Knowing your abilities, I'm sure you already have my address. Shall we say seven o'clock?"

"I have no desire to have dinner with you, Lang Sterling," she got out seethingly, searching desperately for a way to get a handle on the horribly deteriorating situation. She stood to lose all the ground she had so painstakingly gained and she didn't know how to prevent the impending disaster.

"Don't you want to wrap me up in a tidy little bundle for your firm?" he drawled, starting for the door. "I still have patents to sell and you still represent a firm which wants to buy them. Nothing has changed as far as I can see . . ."

He was right, Kali thought frantically. And he was almost at the door. "Lang, wait!"

He turned politely, one red-brown brow cocked inquiringly. He was so damn sure of himself now! Well, she'd managed him successfully last night and she could do so again. Things had gotten a bit rough this morning but that was hardly her fault. She'd done the best she could under the unexpected circumstance of finding Davis Wakefield at her door. In fact, her only tactical error was in having let Lang make her lose her temper. The situation was still salvageable.

"If you really want to talk business, I'll accept your invitation," she said as coolly and calmly as possible.

"I thought you would," he said easily, and turned back toward the door. "By the way, if you're feeling a little annoyed at the moment, console yourself with the thought of how hard it's going to be to get a taxi when I'm dressed like this at eight o'clock in the morning!" As if that remark made him remember something else, he quickly checked his jacket pocket, drawing out a slim wallet and glancing hurriedly inside. "Well, at least you didn't roll me for the credit cards. I appreciate that."

Speechless from her fury, Kali was forced to watch silently as the door shut behind him.

CHAPTER FOUR

"He's almost completely impossible, Mike!" Kali tossed down the copies of Lang's patents which she had been studying. The sheets of drawings and descriptions settled in disarray on her desktop. "Honestly, if it wasn't for the evidence on those pages, you'd have a tough time convincing me the man had evolved more than two steps beyond an amoeba! He seems to run on dumb male instinct, an outdated sense of machismo, and an associated ego problem!"

On the other side of the desk, Mike Jarvis smiled knowingly. "You're the one who told me in the beginning that a creature with all those weaknesses should be easy to handle!"

She glared at him, unable to conceal the unwilling spark of humor in her eyes as she considered the young man sitting across from her. "Just remember, Michael Jarvis, you can be replaced!"

"No, no, Kali," he denied soothingly, blue eyes echoing her amusement, "*you're* the one who can be replaced, remember? That's why you hired me!"

"There are a few drawbacks to modern, progressive management styles," she complained with a small chuckle as she picked up another folder labeled "Sterling."

Mike grinned back. At twenty-six his pleasant features and easygoing manners sometimes hid the razor-sharp mind and enthusiastic ambition. But Kali had spotted both in her initial interview. She had deliberately begun looking for someone who could be groomed for her role or a similar one soon after she'd settled into the vice-presidency. Training one's successor took a bit of courage because there was always an illusion of safety in making oneself seem indispensable to a firm, but in the long run it usually paid off.

On the one hand, management appreciated the security of knowing there would be someone else available to fill a difficult role if the original person in the position chose to leave. The one who took pains to train a successor had the advantage of appearing concerned with the overall well-being of the firm, not merely himself or herself. It was a useful image to foster, although there were some unavoidable risks. The threat of discovering one had inadvertently trained a young shark who might slash the trainer at the first opportunity in hopes of succeeding to the position earlier than scheduled paled into insignificance compared with the advantages of looking progressive and concerned with the company's future in the eyes of management.

Another lesson she owed to Davis Wakefield, Kali privately acknowledged. At that thought the papers in her hands seemed to crinkle beneath her tightening fingers. Deliberately she forced herself to relax. She was still in charge, both of herself and the business at hand.

"How did things go last night?" Mike asked, his expression sobering.

"Not as well as I had hoped," Kali sighed. Her lips

curved wryly. "I think I misjudged the Scotch intake," she admitted. "My only accomplishment in the past twenty-four hours was to discover that Hadley Industrial Systems is our chief competitor."

Mike winced. "I've heard of them . . ."

"You've more than merely heard of them," Kali told him calmly. "Everything I'm teaching you, I learned from their new CEO."

"Oh." He looked a little nonplussed for an instant but his bright mind picked up the implications immediately. "In other words you're in competition with your old mentor?"

"Something like that," she admitted. "I managed to put a small dent in the potential relationship between Sterling and Hadley Industrial, but it wasn't a major destruction job."

"Well, that's something at least . . ."

"I don't know. If Sterling decides to swallow a little pride he can easily make a new beginning with Hadley. At the moment he's not too thrilled with IAI. He had visions of getting us into a bidding war with Hadley."

Mike smiled again. "The man can't be all that dumb. From Sterling's point of view that makes a lot of sense."

"Don't you think I realize that? I was hoping to get him signed, sealed, and delivered before he had a chance to shop around." She waved the folder in her hand meaningfully. "He can't afford to sit back too long and let the various suitors for his hand squabble indefinitely."

"I took a look at the data earlier. He does appear to be enjoying the prospects of his potential prosperity," Mike observed.

"You can say that again! He's living like an impoverished Regency nobleman who's just discovered a distant uncle has died and left him a fortune and a title! Look at this! One of those exotic, new DeLorean sports cars is on order at an automobile dealer's over in Bellevue, he's been living on credit cards for the past month, he's been escorting women like Gwen Mather, *expensive* women, for weeks, and there's a couple of cases of one of the world's most expensive brands of Scotch being imported for him by a local distributor! Not to mention the new clothes! The evening outfit he had on last night was not rented, believe me . . ."

"The Scotch," Mike interjected with a sudden frown. "That's the second time you've mentioned the Scotch. The man doesn't have a drinking problem, does he? Even the most brilliant inventor isn't going to do us much good if he's a lush . . ."

Kali shook her head firmly. "No, there's no indication he's got a problem. That sort of thing would have come out very quickly in the initial research we did. He *does* drink Scotch when he drinks and judging from the stuff he's got on order, he likes the best."

"You implied that last night he'd had too much . . . ?"

"Last night," Kali said deliberately, "was a special occasion. He was celebrating." She met Mike's blank look. "His birthday," she explained politely.

"I see," he replied, still looking a little blank.

Kali burst out laughing. "I wish I had! I certainly didn't make sufficient allowance for Lang Sterling's desire to celebrate his birthday in proper style! Oh, well, I've got another chance to talk sense to him, and this time I shall try to improve my approach."

"How did you wangle the dinner invitation?" Mike demanded curiously.

Kali's mouth turned downward in a grimace. "I've been asking myself that same question since yesterday morning. I thought for a while I'd really blown the whole deal but he still seems to want to negotiate. I can only conclude he's getting a bit anxious about all the bills which will be coming due soon. And he'd probably like to take delivery on that DeLorean as soon as possible . . ."

Kali devoted an unusual amount of time to the selection of her attire for the all-important dinner. Determined to strike exactly the right note, she eyed and discarded a small pinstripe suit as being too businesslike, a silk sheath as being too dressy, and a pair of evening pants as making her appear too aggressive.

Muttering imprecations about inventors who didn't know how to deal with the real world of commerce, she finally chose a textured evening suit done in a sophisticated but quiet brown and black. The plaid cashmere skirt, paisley silk blouse, and embroidered jacket struck just the right note for an evening of business. Paired with bronze pumps and a tiny pair of bronze earrings, the total effect was just what she wanted. Kali braided her hair and twisted it into a sleek, neat knot at her nape, and pronounced herself satisfied. The phone rang as she stepped away from the mirror.

"Yes?" she answered coolly, aware of the fact that it could be Davis on the other end.

"You are coming tonight, aren't you?" Lang's gritty, laconic tones didn't quite conceal a hint of wariness.

"Of course," Kali said quickly. "I have all the facts and figures of the IAI deal to present to you. I think you'll be impressed with the total offer . . ."

"Good. I didn't want to open the Cabernet unnecessarily," he interrupted, sounding relieved. "I'll see you in half an hour."

The phone was hung up in her ear. Drawing a calming breath, Kali lifted her chin and composed herself in patience. She was, she reminded herself, dealing with an inventor and they were notorious for being somewhat eccentric. Picking up the small purse which matched the pumps, she headed for the door.

Lang Sterling's address was in the lively and eclectic neighborhood of Capitol Hill. It was an area Kali knew well, having lived there herself until her recent move into a waterfront high rise. The area was filled with apartment houses, many in charming old Victorian brick, some of the city's most imaginative restaurants, and a collection of intriguing shops. It was a portion of the city popular with the upwardly mobile white-collar crowd.

Although there was an abundance of apartment buildings in the area, Lang's address turned out to be an older house of uncertain vintage nestled on a tree-lined street. Kali parked the Porsche in front of the somewhat overgrown lawn and made her way cautiously up a small flight of rickety wooden steps to an old-fashioned front porch. With a feeling of even greater caution, she rang the doorbell.

When there was no immediate answer, she rang it again, frowning slightly as she wondered if she had the right address after all. Then, with a surprisingly ponderous movement, the door opened. Kali found herself staring in astonishment into an empty hall. There was no one behind the door.

"You are most welcome. Please come in."

The metallic, monotone voice emanating from somewhere near the level of her waist made Kali gasp and jump back a step, one hand going instinctively to her startled, open mouth.

A stocky, rounded creature of metal and plastic stood blinking at her with a cameralike eye. It held open the door with a metal claw which consisted of three fingerlike attachments. As she looked down at it in mingled surprise and rueful acceptance of the extent of Lang's eccentricity, the brightly painted creature rolled backward into the hall, obviously inviting her inside.

"Th . . . thank you. I think," Kali managed, telling herself that what she was viewing wasn't really all that unexpected. The technology for this sort of thing certainly existed. Who should know that better than she? Good grief, anyone who didn't believe in robots owed himself a trip to Disneyland where they could be seen in action any day of the week! For that matter, they had even been made available in the Christmas catalog of an exclusive Texas department store. The ultimate toy for the person who had everything . . .

She was stepping slowly over the threshold, staring in fascination at the small robot, when Lang appeared, wiping his hands briskly on a kitchen towel.

"Ah, there she is! Thanks, Nalg, you can go back to the kitchen. Come on into the living room, Madame Vice-President, I've got a nice warming glass of wine waiting for you. It's cold out there!"

"I wonder if you could perhaps avoid calling me by that particular title for the remainder of the evening." In spite of her resolve, Kali's teeth had set in annoyance at his blithe words.

"Of course, of course! What title would you prefer?" He grinned wickedly, leading her into a room which proved another surprise for Kali. It was furnished with some of the best antiques she had ever seen.

The house, she quickly observed, had not been done with any one period in mind. Instead, it looked as if the dominant goal had been to create a warm background aimed at providing a man with great comfort. Heavy, solid furniture, a lot of polished wooden table surfaces littered with magazines, and a cheerfully blazing fireplace comprised an extraordinarily comfortable room with an undertone of romantic age. Underneath an Oriental carpet provided a subtle, exotic touch.

The place was also quite clean. Kali wondered how much of that was due to the little robot's efforts. A creature like that could prove useful around the house!

"How about calling me by my name?" she responded dryly to Lang's question. She took one of the high-backed wing chairs which would have looked at home in the library of a nineteenth-century English house and slanted a glance at her host.

"Kali it is," he agreed, coming toward her with a glass of wine he had poured at an Irish mahogany sideboard. He handed her the crystal glass and raised his own in a polite gesture.

In this old-fashioned, rather romantic room, his eyes looked quite green, Kali thought vaguely as she followed his lead and took a sip of the heavy, dark wine. The gleaming color behind the thick lashes made her uneasy in a way she was at a loss to describe. He seemed to fit the room, came an unbidden realization. There was an other-world, other-age look to him which was hard to define. The white cotton broadcloth shirt was sufficiently twentieth century but there was something about the way he wore it: open-collared with square, gold cuff links, which gave him a faintly piratical appearance. The dark slacks were unabashedly close-fitting and the soft leather belt had a bold, embossed buckle. The polished toe of a dark leather dress boot gleamed beneath the bottom edge of the pants.

What was really beginning to bother her, Kali decided grimly, wasn't the way Lang Sterling looked, but what her imagination tended to do with his appearance! Why couldn't the man look like what he was, a roboticist?

"I'm pleased you're willing to finally get down to business, Lang," Kali began determinedly as he lounged

71

across from her in the library chair which matched her own. "I can assure you that Interactive Automation is . . ."

"Later," he interrupted with magnificently calm authority. "I never talk business before dinner."

Kali arched one brow behind the frames of her glasses but obediently shut up and took another sip of wine. Then she tried another approach. "You have a fascinating collection of furniture in this room . . ."

He eyed her for a long moment as if assessing the reason behind the comment. Then he smiled in blatant pleasure. "Thank you. It's going to get a lot better, though, after I sell those patents. I hate to admit this, but that chair in which you're sitting is a reproduction. So is that Georgian secretary."

"You're going to replace the reproductions with the genuine articles as soon as you can?" Automatically Kali glanced around with interest.

"The credit limits on my credit cards aren't high enough to allow me to start investing in the furniture I want," he drawled. "That project will have to wait until I get paid outright for my inventions."

"IAI will be willing to advance you . . ."

He waved her to a frustrated halt. "Please don't bring up that name until after dinner."

"You started the discussion!" she retorted, irritated.

"Did I?" he asked innocently, sipping his wine. "I don't know what got into me."

"Something about the sight of me makes you think of business, I expect!" she murmured pointedly.

"Not quite," he contradicted thoughtfully. He hesitated and then asked curiously, "How much do you know about me, Kali?"

She stifled a flush, terribly afraid for a moment that he knew of the various credit checks and reference investiga-

tions she'd done on him. No, he couldn't possibly
. . .

"My engineers have explained the revolutionary ad-
vances in sensor systems you've come up with. I know you
worked for a computer software firm for a few years after
you graduated from college and that you also have some
background in electrical and mechanical engineering
. . ." she began politely.

"I don't mean that sort of thing, I mean what do you
know about me personally?" Legs thrust out in front of
him, he leaned back into the depths of the chair, cradling
his wineglass in two hands.

Kali glanced at the glass and her lip twitched. "I know
you generally prefer Scotch."

He laughed at that, bronze-green eyes gleaming with his
amusement. "After the other night I decided a temporary
change of pace was in order. I had one hell of a headache
yesterday morning, you know."

"Did you?"

"Ummm. And walking out into your living room to find
another man there didn't do much for it!"

"I did *not* set that situation up, Lang," Kali told him
coolly and deliberately. "I had no idea Davis would show
up so unexpectedly."

"But you were sharp enough to play the situation as
interestingly as possible when the circumstances were
forced upon you." He didn't seem upset by it any longer,
merely somewhat admiring, she decided.

"You don't know Davis Wakefield," she said quietly.
"The fact that he was at my door so early that morning
means he had every intention of trying to set up a useful
situation of his own. The temptation to turn the tables on
him was irresistible, I'm afraid."

"I believe you," he said unexpectedly, nodding once.
"And if I hadn't been concerned on a future financial

73

basis, I might even have appreciated the little byplay. As it is . . ." He lifted one shoulder in rueful resignation.

"Are . . . are you going to make another approach to Hadley?" she ventured.

"That's business. I'm not talking business. I'd rather hear something about you, Kali Havelock. Tell me about your relationship with Wakefield. Were you deeply in love with him when he dumped you?"

"*Dumped me!* That's a rather callous way of describing an engagement that was broken off!" she protested.

"He looked like a man capable of doing callous things. Cold."

Kali's smoky eyes narrowed consideringly. "Do you think so? I never thought about it quite like that. Davis is very bright, very good at what he does . . ."

"I'd be willing to bet he doesn't have an ounce of honest passion in him, except whatever passion it takes to get to the top." The declaration was made with such absolute conviction that Kali didn't quite know what to say.

"You don't even know him," she managed weakly.

"You do. Are you going to contradict me? Do you look back on the period of your engagement as one laced with adventure and desire? Did the man make your blood race when he took you in his arms? Do you still lie awake at nights occasionally thinking of him?"

"Good grief! That's hardly any of your business!"

"I spent half of last night lying awake thinking about the way you had felt in my arms, Kali," he murmured.

"I can't imagine why!" she retorted roundly, unwilling to be put on the defensive again. "I certainly slept soundly enough myself!" That wasn't precisely true, but then she'd had a lot on her mind. *Business* matters!

"A little robot," he acknowledged blandly. "Except that, for a while, at least, you weren't at all robotic. I really am sorry about all that Scotch, Kali," he went on sadly.

74

"If I'd had a clearer head we could have found out just how unrobotic you really are."

"Mr. Sterling, if you're going to sidetrack this conversation into purely personal areas . . ."

"Do you love Davis Wakefield?"

"No! But that, damn it, is none of your business!"

"Were you ever in love with him or was it more a pact between two robots?"

Kali found herself wanting to scream. Not for the world would she now admit to him that her relationship with Davis Wakefield had been disappointingly cool from the start, that he had treated their engagement as more of a business alliance. Which was exactly what it had turned out to be, she recalled raggedly.

"You say you do not care to discuss business matters, Lang," she got out coldly. "I do not care to discuss personal ones. Is that clear?"

He sighed. "Very. I suppose that means there's nothing left to do but eat . . . Nalg?" He called the robot's name and there was a quiet little whirr of a motor as the creature rolled into view from the kitchen. "How are the potatoes doing?"

"They are burning," the metallic voice announced politely.

"Burning!" Lang was on his feet, racing for the kitchen. Almost simultaneously Kali caught a whiff of burned potato. Curiously she rose to follow her suddenly exasperated host. Nalg rolled on into the kitchen behind the humans and watched with a dispassionate eye as Lang yanked the sizzling pot of potatoes off the stove and dumped out the contents.

"Damn it, Nalg, you scrambled-circuit idiot, why didn't you tell me they were burning?"

"I informed you of the status of the potatoes as soon as you requested information on them."

"I don't know what the hell you're laughing at," Lang growled at Kali, who was shaking with silent humor. "You're the one who will have to help me eat burned potatoes!"

"I can't help it! Nalg sounds so politely self-righteous and you look so disgusted with what is only a machine . . ." She broke off as light dawned. And then a slow smile curved her mouth. "Nalg . . . Nalg . . . Oh, my goodness . . . !"

Lang cast her a suspicious glance as he ran water into the singed pan.

"Nalg is an anagram of Lang, isn't it? You mixed up the letters of your own name and named your creation after yourself!" Kali laughed. "Do you think of Nalg as a sort of son?"

"Don't be ridiculous!"

But there was a red stain high on his cheekbones and Lang spent several moments earnestly making last-minute dinner preparations while Kali watched, amused and satisfied at having gotten a little of her own back for his demanding questions about Davis Wakefield.

When at last they sat down to dinner at the old, claw-footed oak table there was a new ease in the atmosphere. It was as if Kali's laughter had broken some strange barrier and left both of them feeling more relaxed.

While Nalg served with all the dignity of a professional butler, Lang and Kali found themselves deep in a conversation that started out on the subject of antiques and wound up covering everything from U.S. foreign policy to favorite Seattle restaurants. By mutual but unspoken agreement they avoided the topics of robots, patents, and Davis Wakefield.

The candles in the Irish crystal holders had burned very low by the time Nalg had carefully removed the last of the dishes with his amazingly agile three-fingered claw. When

76

the robot returned carrying a bottle of aromatic after-dinner spirits and poured the liquid into a small snifter, Kali finally became aware of an interesting fact.

"You know, I don't think Nalg has let my glass get empty all evening! Have you programmed him to get me drunk?" she asked, laughing across the white lace table-cloth.

"Nalg is a very literal being. I told him to keep fluid levels relatively stable in all glassware while you and I are seated at the table and he's been doing his job. He's programmed to watch for the halfway mark in each glass. Stop drinking and he'll stop pouring!"

"Is that a hint that I'm getting tipsy?" She smiled demurely.

"My dear little vice-president," Lang intoned in a velvety drawl, "I would give a great deal to see you tipsy. Shall we take our snifters into the living room? Nalg will do the dishes."

Kali found herself following obediently, distantly aware that the tension between them had softened, grown muted and warm during the course of dinner. She knew she had wound up telling him more about herself than she had planned.

With a wine-induced clarity she realized she had some-how wanted to impress him a little. Her career, which had been on a straight upward path since college and which she had made a focal point of her existence, *was* impressive! She excelled at what she did and Kali faced the fact that she had wanted Lang to know that. Wanted him to know that, in her own field, she was as intelligent as he was in his.

It was important to her that the men she dated genuinely respected her intellect and abilities. Dated? This wasn't a date, this was a business evening! Ruefully she tried to pull her thoughts back in line.

77

"Now what are you smiling about?" Lang demanded softly as he threw another log on the fire and found a record for the sleek, low-profile stereo system.

Perhaps it was the wine or perhaps it was the sensual rhythms of the classical guitar music which began to drift through the room. Perhaps it was simply a streak of unexpected honesty. Whatever the cause, Kali regretted the words as soon as they left her mouth.

"I was thinking that I want to be loved for my mind."

She recovered herself almost instantly, summoning a droll expression which subtly asked him to share the little joke.

To her chagrin Lang didn't respond on an amused level as he came to sit beside her on the chintz-covered Louis XVI–style sofa. "Because you're more confident of your intellectual abilities than you are of your physical attractions or your potential for genuine passion?"

Kali recoiled, shocked both by the words and the possibility of their reality. "No! You misunderstand, I . . ."

"I, on the other hand," he continued slowly, each word measured as he picked up his snifter of after-dinner liqueur and cradled it, "would like to be loved for something other than my intellectual abilities."

She stared at him, aware of the intensity behind his statement and uncertain how to deal with it. The intimate, sensual atmosphere induced by the other-world room, the hypnotic qualities of the blazing fire, and the ravishing guitar music seemed to create a state of unusual honesty. She didn't understand it but it was difficult not to respond to it.

"I'm sure you must want respect for your achievements," Kali finally managed carefully.

"Perhaps. But I sure as hell don't want to be loved for them!"

"But your intellect is an important part of you, Lang."

"When you talk about my intellect you really mean my work in robotics, right?" he challenged softly, bronze-green eyes lifting to meet hers with glimmering directness.

"Well, yes, it's what you're known for, your area of expertise . . ."

"And the way in which I'll make my money," he concluded bluntly. He watched her from beneath his lashes as if debating whether or not to finish his comment. Then he seemed to come to a decision. "But the man who's going to make his fortune with machines isn't the real *me*, Kali. It's a realization I've been homing in on for the past couple of years and now I'm very certain of it."

"That doesn't make any sense, Lang. Of course you're that man. You can't separate yourself from your skills and abilities . . ."

"And furthermore, you can't understand why I should even want to do so," he finished for her with a perception that rankled.

Kali frowned. "You're being very cryptic."

He shut his eyes for a moment and then opened them to study her. "I know. I really can't explain any more this evening. Instead I would rather give you a more graphic demonstration of what I'm talking about."

He took her by surprise with a soft rush that somehow removed the snifter from her hand, the glasses from her face, and caught her up gently in his arms.

"Kali Havelock," he said huskily, "I don't give a damn that you're a vice-president at Interactive Automation, Inc. I don't care that you're in a position to offer me a great sum of money. I don't care that you've proven you can manipulate me. There is something about you which fascinates me. I came down that staircase the other night only because I couldn't resist the fascination. I want you. I want to take you to bed and make passionate love to you until you can't even remember that you're only here tonight because I built a better robot! Until you can only think of me, the *real* me!"

Speechless with amazement, Kali found herself staring up at him, smoky eyes wide and startled. She was frantically trying to decide how best to handle the situation when he drastically reduced her options by taking her lips in an overpowering, deeply compelling kiss.

CHAPTER FIVE

She had been half-prepared for the pass, Kali realized
vaguely as she braced herself against the onslaught. The
fact that he had made it wasn't what amazed her. What
amazed her was her reaction to it now that the situation
was upon her.

There was a strange, overriding curiosity in her, a very
feminine curiosity that wanted to know more about what
it was like to be kissed by a man who claimed not to care
a jot about who she was or what she had accomplished.
And she wanted to know, too, whether he would kiss her
sober with the same overwhelming sensuality he had
shown while high on the Scotch.

In that moment Kali could not have explained the dangerous curiosity. She only knew that, for a few minutes at
least, she was going to succumb to it. Time enough later
to call a halt . . .

The palms of her hands settled on his shoulders, amber
nails sinking into the white broadcloth of his shirt. Lang
held her easily at first, his hands gliding slowly from her
nape to the sensitive area at the small of her back. His

mouth moved on hers with a persuasive warmth that was taking on the aspect of a compulsion.

"You're a dangerous woman, Kali," he rasped a little thickly against her lips.

"No," she whispered, the denial muffled as he sealed her mouth once more. *No,* she went on silently. *I'm not dangerous, not in a man's arms. Perhaps in the executive suite, perhaps in a business confrontation, but not* this *way!*

Then her thoughts began to scatter in a manner that might prove truly dangerous—to herself. For under the heat of his kiss she found herself postponing the moment when she must break off the passionate assault.

She felt the edge of his tongue tracing the outline of her parted lips and she shivered when the probing touch reached farther inward. There was a languorous, inevitable sensation about the slow coupling of their mouths. Kali's fingertips sank more deeply into the material of his shirt.

Lang's hold tightened in the same moment that he thrust his tongue completely into her yielding warmth and she heard the groan which emanated from deep in his chest. There was a seductive quality about his evident desire, Kali discovered.

When he began a kneading, rippling movement up the length of her spine she trembled and found herself sinking toward him. His fingers clenched and unclenched in the soft contours of her slender back and her head tipped to one side, falling languidly onto his shoulder.

It wasn't until she felt his fingers in her hair, loosening the braided coil at the back of her head, that she made some attempt to struggle back to reality.

"Lang? Wait, please . . ."

"Kali, I want you. I can't wait. There's no need . . ."

His lips tracked a line of damp fire along the length of

82

her jaw and down her throat as the jungle-cat mass of hair came free beneath his touch. She moaned softly as he wound his fingers tightly in the thickness of the tendrils, anchoring her more completely against his shoulder.

"Oh, Lang!"

"Don't think about it," he advised huskily and then refastened his mouth on hers while he slipped off the jacket of the brown and black suit. It was as if he used the impact of his kiss to chain her for the moment and when it was over Kali knew she was somehow far more vulnerable. The silky paisley blouse seemed no protection at all from the heat of his body and the questing touch of his hands.

The romantic, emotion-arousing music of the classical guitar swirled around them as Lang lay back on the sofa with Kali cradled at his side. Bracing himself on one elbow, he looked down at her softened, half-parted lips and heavy lashes. The bronze-green eyes meshed and held her smoky gaze with hypnotic bonds as he deliberately brought one hand up along her hip, across the length of her ribs, and finally closed it firmly over one breast.

When he made the final, intimate contact, Kali broke the spell of his eyes, turning her face into his chest with a small exclamation which had no verbal meaning.

"There is no Scotch fogging my mind tonight, Kali," he whispered thickly as his palm moved in a slight, scraping movement across the tip of her breast. "I'm going to undress you here in the firelight, watch your hair fall around your shoulders, see the color of your skin in the glow of the flames. And then I'm going to carry you to my bed and make you mine."

She stirred restlessly beneath the intent of his words, knowing she should stop him while she still could. But when she would have spoken he moved his fingers from her breast to her lips, shushing her with urgent tenderness.

"No, sweetheart, don't say anything. Just cling to me and let it all happen the way it was meant to happen."

"Lang, this isn't what I wanted tonight . . . !" she got out, closing her lashes against the wave of inevitability.

"I know," he breathed, his fingers finding the buttons of the paisley blouse. "I know. You wanted a dry, cold business deal but I can't even think about business around you. Don't you understand?"

Kali sucked in her breath but whatever she would have said dissolved into a meaningless protest in her brain as he pulled the blouse free of the skirt and finished unfastening the last button. The heat of his hand was a fiery summons as he flattened it boldly against the skin of her stomach.

Her head arched back over his arm and Kali moaned breathlessly as Lang put his lips to the pulse at the base of her throat. Slowly he explored the small curve of her breasts above the lacy line of bra. Kali's legs shifted with an uneasy restlessness and her fingers found the dark russet hair just above his collar. She clenched as wave after wave of shivering passion began to wash along her nerve endings.

It was a sensation unlike any she had ever known. No man had ever had quite this staggering effect on her senses. Her relationships in the past had been admirable examples of the best in modern male-female associations. She knew there had always been an element of distance in those relationships, a cool equality based on mutual respect and common goals.

There was no distance possible with Lang and Kali didn't know how to handle that lack. With every movement, every caress, he was making it manifestly clear he wanted her to abandon herself completely to him. He wanted to ravish her senses, seduce her, make love to her in a way that left no room for any element of cool distance. Kali knew a kind of primitive fear at the back of her mind.

If she allowed herself to be swept into the whirlpool of desire she would be running a risk such as she had never really known.

That same tingling, exciting fear warned that this man did not seek merely a satisfaction of the senses; he wanted to *possess* her. He wanted to embroil them both in a blazing affair which, even if it lasted only one night, would burn itself into her very being.

All this Kali sensed. She was vividly aware of the reckless danger awaiting her and yet that very danger seemed yet another inducement to her passions, whirling them into a chaotic storm which knew Lang as its center.

Her lacy bra fell away as Lang found the closure. Then he bent to kiss the hardening peaks of her breasts. Kali flinched from the searing heat of his mouth as he caught one nipple lightly and tugged it to even greater erection.

She gasped as he refused to allow her time to grow accustomed to the marauding pull of his lips on her breast. She wanted to draw back a little, learn to handle the almost unbearable throbbing tautness, allow her body an opportunity to adjust.

But when he felt her unspoken resistance, Lang responded by tightening the grip of his mouth, letting his teeth graze raspingly on the ultra-sensitized nipple until Kali moaned heavily with the unexpected impact on her senses.

"Don't fight it, darling," he begged as he transferred his attention to the other nipple. "Surrender to it. Surrender to *me*. I need you so badly tonight!"

Kali couldn't explain why in that moment she was succumbing to his urging. She only knew it was easier and far more tempting to do as he said rather than salvage the evening. When his hand unzipped the cashmere skirt, slid down the silky pantyhose, and removed her bronze pumps, she found herself at work on the buttons of his shirt rather than forming the protest she knew she should be making.

She heard his indrawn breath as he surveyed her almost completely nude body in the flickering firelight but her attention was riveted by the mass of curling hair on his chest as she freed his shirt and pushed the edges aside.

And then, drawn by the magnetism of his hard body, she lowered her head to kiss the line of his shoulder and track a path toward the flat, masculine nipples.

"Kali, Kali, you're going to send me out of my mind, do you realize that?" he demanded fiercely.

He pulled her onto her side, pressing her against him. With probing, exquisitely sensitive fingers he found the curve of her buttocks.

"Oh!"

Kali's small exclamation was wrenched from far back in her throat as he squeezed gently and then slid a hand boldly under the edge of her small panties.

She wrapped her arms around his waist, burying her face against his chest, as he explored the narrow cleft in her derriere, tracing an unbelievably sensuous path down to the softening warmth between her legs.

He groaned, retracing his way back up to the base of her spine, and then he began the incredibly arousing caress over again. This time when he reached the warm core of her femininity he lingered to draw tiny patterns of pleasure there.

Kali's amber-tinted nails sank deeply into the muscles of his back as she tried to catch her breath. It was only when she heard the growl and felt it beneath her lips as she kissed his chest that she realized just how fiercely she must be scoring his flesh.

"All this passion in you," he grated, his mouth against her curving shoulder. "You're going to tear me apart tonight, do you realize that? I'll never be the same!"

86

It was she who would never be the same! But Kali didn't know how to pull back from the edge of the cliff. She felt committed to the threatening end. Every time he touched her, kissed her, he seemed to be entangling her more completely in the web. She could only respond and explore and experience. There was no ceasing the headlong flight which had begun.

"Lang, I think I'm going crazy," she whispered, gliding a palm down to the waistband of his slacks.

"That's the way it's supposed to be. God! I love the feel of your hands on me, little one. Touch me some more, undress me . . ."

Slowly, fumblingly, she found the buckle of his belt, unclasping it and reaching for the zipper beneath it. He drew in his stomach at her touch, his uncompromising desire bold and passionately aggressive.

She undressed him, feeling awkward. But when the last of his clothing had been dropped to the Oriental carpet beside the sofa she heard his deep sigh of satisfaction. With heavy passion he arched her against him, pulling her hips forcefully, deeply into his.

She felt his full arousal pressed at her thigh, letting her know the extent of its waiting strength. Kali trembled, clinging to him, her lashes soft on her cheek.

For a moment they lay like that, absorbing the feel of each other, and then Lang moved, rising slowly to his feet and tugging her up beside him. Kali blinked at him in the firelight, feeling shaky and uncertain of her balance.

When she lifted her questioning face to his he locked his fists in her tangled, flowing mane and kissed her fiercely. Without breaking the kiss he slid his arms down, swinging her off her feet and high against his chest.

Holding her with the chain of the kiss, he carried her down the hall and into a large bedroom which was completely dominated by the most massive four-poster bed

Kali had ever seen. She was vaguely aware of the dark, masculine antique furniture of the dimly lit room but there was no time to examine it closely. She only knew that somehow the environment once again suited its owner, creating the other-world atmosphere in which he seemed so at home.

"I feel as if I've just carried off a woman and am on the verge of making her my own." Slowly, his eyes never loosing hers, Lang settled Kali onto the thick, puffy quilt.

"Men . . ." Kali licked her lips, seeking the right words. "Men don't carry off women anymore. The women go willingly or not at all." She knew with some disturbing flash of common sense that she needed to register the statement. It was not at all safe to let him think he had seduced her and carried her off into the night. What small protection remained for her lay in making it clear that what was happening this evening was by mutual consent and mutual passion.

He laughed, a low, husky sound of growing certainty, and then he was down beside her, gathering her close. "Tell me the truth," he coaxed, nibbling and teasing her ear while his hand strayed over her breasts and his fingertips feathered over her abdomen down to her secret warmth. "Did you plan to end up in my bed tonight?"

"Lang!" The name was a protest and she tried to draw back. But when she moved, her legs parted slightly and his prowling hand found her in the most tantalizing of touches. She gasped.

He made a sound of deep pleasure, snarling his heavy legs with hers. Once more he touched his mouth to the crested peaks of her small breasts and Kali thought she would go out of her head with the need he was instilling.

Clutching at him, she found the hard, muscled length of his deliciously rough thigh, then her hand stroked him in intimate wonder.

For long, floating moments they caressed each other, learning each other's secrets and needs until the mounting sexual tension threatened to engulf them both. Kali knew beyond any doubt that Lang was as genuinely and as deeply aroused as she was. There was no hint of him playing some kind of sophisticated bedroom game with her. The level of passion was potent and primitive and, perhaps because of that, utterly irresistible.

She only knew she wanted him with a desire which went beyond anything she had ever experienced. Her blood raced in her veins, her head spun with a space traveler's vertigo, and her body literally ached for the final possession. Never before had she thought of sex as an act of possession!

"I want you," Kali whispered with an honesty which should have amazed her but didn't in that sensual atmosphere. "Oh, Lang, make love to me. I want you so badly . . . !"

"I'm going to make you mine tonight, my darling," he vowed, turning her gently on her back. "By morning there won't be any going back for either of us!"

In the pale light filtering in from the hall Kali had a glimpse of the tautly drawn planes of his face as he loosened his hold on her for a moment to pull open the nearby bedside drawer. She was vaguely aware of the fact that he still retained enough common sense to think of the future. She hadn't even considered the full extent of the physical risks she was running tonight. His decision to take precautions touched her.

But she couldn't find any words with which to thank him as he came back to her, lifting himself and settling onto her body with agonizing slowness. In her need Kali pulled at him, her cries of urgency soft kitten sounds in her throat.

But he prolonged the moment, lying full length on top

89

of her, impressing her body with his weight and hardness while he feathered tiny kisses across her face, shoulders, and breasts.

"Lang!"

Her legs slid apart of their own accord on the quilt as she opened herself to him. The soles of her feet rode up and down his calves in an effort to close the final distance.

"You're like a handful of fire," he whispered wonderingly. "Silk and fire." Then he moved against her with a slow, erotic power that stilled the breath in her for a long instant.

Her body tightened under the impact of his possession and her nails dug violently into the muscles of his shoulders. Kali's eyes widened with sudden realization.

What was happening was not just a moment of exquisite passion; it was an act of claiming and she was the one being claimed. The truth of that sang with warning throughout her body, blotting out all else. In the stillness which followed his act of mastery she found herself staring wordlessly up into emerald eyes that flamed with the same knowledge. She was his in that instant. Neither of them would ever be the same.

There were no words to exchange, no rationalizations which could be offered in that tension-filled time. For another few seconds Lang stared deeply down into her eyes and then he began to move in a throbbing, building, spiraling rhythm which commanded a response.

With a shuddering sigh Kali gave herself up to that rhythm, letting it whirl her away to a distant place. Safe in Lang's arms, or perhaps trapped there, she freed herself to the passion which sought to take her completely. The tightening sensation in her lower body became a dynamic force demanding release.

As if he knew the extent of that force, Lang stoked it, fed it, teased it, and channeled it. Kali clung to him and when the mind-spinning end finally came upon her in a flowing rush she wasn't even aware of the sharp manner in which her teeth nipped at Lang's perspiration-damp shoulder.

He held her fiercely while the feverish tremors wracked her body and she knew he was taking a surging satisfaction in her own gratification. Then she felt him let himself go, heard his stifled shout, knew the abrupt, arching tautness of his body. It was her turn to hold him with a lover's violence. Then they crumpled into the quilt in a breathless sprawl.

Countless moments later Kali began to float back to reality. Only to find she really wasn't in a mood to face it. Every instinct warned that there was too much to be dealt with, too much to be analyzed. It was safer and far more pleasant to stay awhile longer in this soft world with the blurred edges. Vaguely she gazed up at the ceiling, fighting the return of the real world.

Lang's heavy body moved, sliding off her until he lay stretched out beside Kali, propped on his elbow. The dark russet hair was lazily, attractively tousled and the bronze-green eyes were warm with satisfaction and a strange gentleness.

"Don't move," he whispered, bending his head to drop a quick kiss on her softly bruised mouth.

Kali stared uncomprehendingly as he rolled off the bed, got to his feet, and disappeared into the adjoining bath. A moment later she heard water running furiously.

When he reappeared in the bathroom doorway Kali was still waiting, languidly curled on the quilt. Obeying even such a small order from him was a way of postponing the inevitable. She could keep her dream world tucked around her for a little while longer. She'd never lived in dream worlds . . .

Across the short distance he smiled at her, striding

forward with a purposefulness which made her look at him curiously.

"Lang? What are you doing?"

"Trying out my new investment." He grinned engagingly. With a swift, strong motion he reached down to scoop her up into his arms.

"What in the world . . . ?" Dazedly, she clung to him, her hair falling back over his arm, smoky eyes widening as she searched his relaxed, happy face.

"Hush. Close your eyes," he commanded, starting toward the bath.

Once again she obeyed. It was easier that way. Eyes closed she became more aware of the musky scent of him, the drying film of perspiration on his skin, and the faint scratchiness of the hair on his chest as it touched her nude body. She was also aware of the strength in him as he carried her and found it oddly satisfying. Unconsciously she rested her head against his shoulder.

"Where are we going?" she murmured and then her lashes flickered open as he came to a halt. The roar of water surrounded her and she glanced down at the huge Roman tub done in a brick red beneath her. It was nearly filled with water that swirled in great eddies which were driven by small jets around the edges of the tub.

"They just finished installing it last week." Lang chuckled, lowering her into the heated, foaming water. "Got it on the installment plan. But that's okay, I can pay it off completely when I sell those patents!"

Kali blinked owlishly, unable to deny the wonderful sensation of the water as she was seated on the interior built-in tub step. It was heavenly.

"You, uh, have a lot of use for this sort of amenity?" she tried to quip, aware of his hands in her hair. He was catching it back and twisting it into a knot. She could sense him glancing around the bathroom, searching for something with which to hold it.

"I hope to get a great deal of use out of it in the future," Lang murmured meaningfully, reaching out to snag a towel which he deftly wound around her head. "There, that should keep it dry." He slid down beside her into the tub, sighing blissfully. "A stroke of brilliant intuition, hmmm?" he added, indicating his purchase. "I must have known you'd be barging into my life sooner or later."

His lighthearted, enormously pleased expression was difficult to resist and Kali wasn't in a mood to try. "You're like a kid taking delivery on a lot of toys before Christmas actually arrives!" She laughed.

"And enjoying every one of them," he agreed cheerfully, pulling her close. "But you're the best one I've unwrapped so far . . ."

He lowered his head to brush her mouth, a wealth of recent memory and future anticipation in his kiss. Kali couldn't begin to assess or analyze the power of his attraction. She only knew that there in his arms, her body soothed and stimulated by the foaming water, her mind determined to block out the reality of what she was doing, she couldn't resist him.

Slowly, languidly, they led each other through a recuperation period and then, inevitably, toward a new arousal. When Lang's hands began gliding along her body with a new urgency, Kali closed her eyes and nestled close in the roiling water.

"Do you know," he growled huskily, his hand moving along the inside of her thigh with a delicate finesse, "the first time I saw you I had an urge to tear away all your cool poise and self-control and get you into this tub!"

Kali turned her face into his shoulder, her fingers trailing over his knee under the water. "It didn't take you long,

93

did it?" There was a hint of wry resignation in the words which he caught immediately.

"Kali, are you going to fret about that aspect of the situation?" he asked with quick worry. He lifted her head from his shoulder, forcing her eyes to meet his. "Is it going to bother you tomorrow that we came together so easily and so soon?"

She tried to find a cool, sardonic approach but her eyes were beginning to fill with the knowledge of the truth the morning would hold. "Shouldn't it?"

"No!" The gritted denial was emphatic. "Trust me, Kali. It's working out like this because everything is right. You're here tonight because, under all the layers of games and business and maneuvering, we're fascinated by each other. We want each other . . ."

"I'd rather not talk about it," she said very quietly, and reached up to put her fingertips under his firm jaw. Lifting her face, she said very close to his lips, "The morning will take care of itself."

He hesitated and she knew that part of him wanted to argue and another part wanted to take the invitation of her mouth. With the sensual impulse of the water and the rising desire flowing between them, Kali was fairly certain which side of his nature would predominate. She was right.

Lang kissed her, standing up in the water as he did so. Without releasing her mouth, he slipped the towel from her hair and began drying her body. By the time he had finished they were clinging together, the fever of need high in both of them.

Lang spoke only once more as he carried her back to the huge bed.

"Nothing will change in the morning, Kali. You belong to me now and I'm not going to let you go."

Still she said nothing. There was nothing to say. As he

settled her on the quilt Kali reached up to pull him down to her with an urgency which carried overtones of a deeply hidden fear . . .

She awoke a long time later, aware of the weight of Lang's arm across her breasts. Her body felt exhausted and replete. There was also a deep twinge here and there which told her she was going to be a little sore in places in the morning. Lang's lovemaking had been deep, demanding, and complete. He had indeed carried her off into the night.

He might as well have used a large steed so he could have added the final touch of tossing her over the saddle-bow, she thought with a mind that had miraculously cleared during sleep.

Carefully, aware of the need to rescue herself from a situation she couldn't believe she had allowed to happen in the first place, Kali eased out from under the weight of Lang's arm. His hand on her breast tightened for an instant and she went very still, fearing that she'd wakened him.

But he continued to sleep, dark lashes resting quietly on his cheekbones, his harsh face relaxed. When she was again certain it was safe to move, Kali finished her retreat to the edge of the bed and stood up hastily. Her one driving thought was to get away, return to her own home where she could think . . .

She found her clothing where it had been left in the living room and dressed, shivering, in front of the poor heat remaining in the fireplace. It was only as she located her purse and was hurrying toward the door that she remembered Nalg.

The little robot was standing quietly in the kitchen, apparently communing with the wall. The sensor which functioned as an eye followed her as she moved past the door but the creature didn't move.

95

As if it were a living being staring at her, Kali felt obliged to say something.

"Good night, Nalg. Thanks for doing the dishes . . ."

There was no response and Kali realized the machine probably wasn't capable of receiving verbal input or instructions in a voice that wasn't Lang's. It was extremely difficult to program a robot to take verbal input. To a machine the same word sounded entirely different when it was spoken by different voices. So Nalg was probably only capable of responding to his creator's voice. As for the apparent communion he was conducting with a wall . . . Kali smiled crookedly for an instant as she realized the robot was merely plugged into a socket for the night so that its batteries would be recharged by morning.

Kali hurried on toward the front door, her mind beginning to churn as it picked up the clues of the disaster which had befallen her and started putting them together into a coherent whole. The end product was going to be devastating.

CHAPTER SIX

Why?

The question which had been haunting Kali since she'd fled Lang's home in the early hours of the morning came back again and again as she plunged into the work awaiting her at the office.

Why had Lang seduced her? Was it because of a need to placate his male pride? Had he wanted to show her he could manipulate her? Or was it because he thought that if he controlled her physically he could wangle an even better deal out of IAI?

Kali wanted to flinch from each of the possible explanations but she forced herself to face them with typical level-headed determination. His own explanation, that he was simply, overwhelmingly attracted to her, didn't wash. Men weren't simply, overwhelmingly attracted to her, Kali reminded herself grimly.

A perceptive few had shown a proper appreciation for her business capability and talents and during the past few years there had been two or three who had proposed marriage, discounting Davis Wakefield's proposal, of course. But the relationships had been built on such things as respect, admiration, and common interests. There hadn't been a single man to Kali's recollection who had declared he couldn't live without her in his bed.

Not that she wanted such a declaration, she reminded herself violently as she forced her way through a report Mike Jarvis had prepared on the Japanese industry's approach to the use of robots in factories. Other than the fact that the approach varied from the more cautious mood in the United States—which she already knew—Kali was not getting a lot out of the report. She reached out and touched the button of her intercom.

"Joanna, would you track down Mike Jarvis and ask him to come to my office, please?"

"Right away, Kali."

Kali sat tapping the report with an impatient finger, waiting. And while she waited she fought to keep her mind from straying into the realm of the other problem in her life.

"Did you want me, Kali?" Mike sauntered through her doorway a few moments later, a cup of coffee in one hand and a smile on his handsome mouth for Kali's brisk, middle-aged, and highly efficient secretary, Joanna Mills.

"I've read the report on Japan's approach to the use of robots," she began in a businesslike tone. If Mike was surprised by her brusqueness, he managed to conceal it. He flopped into the chair across from her and waited calmly.

"And . . . ?"

"And I think it needs a little more work, Mike. This is supposed to be the basis of an informational booklet aimed at potential customers of Interactive Automation, Inc."

"You said you wanted something which would show them how they could utilize robots in factories . . ."

"I do, and obviously in any such discussion one has to

98

talk about the Japanese approach because they've gone so much farther with it than we have . . ."

"Didn't I cover the subject?" Mike frowned and sipped his coffee.

Kali forced herself to relax and smile. "Mike, what you've done is illustrate how Japanese workers have easily accepted the robot in their midst because they don't have to fear for their jobs. Japanese management has a well-known commitment to its workers. Layoffs are almost unheard of in Japan. When the robots are introduced into the workplace people might get shifted around, but management never lets anyone go . . ."

"And because of that philosophy they've achieved highly flexible, very efficient manufacturing plants," Mike concluded firmly.

"I'm aware of that," she retorted dryly.

Mike had the grace to turn a little red.

"My point is that American management doesn't operate that way. Mike, you can't put out a sales brochure telling the average American manager he can modernize his factory by putting in robots as long as he does things the way the Japanese do them! You're not going to change the way America does business overnight. You've got to sell our product in the real world and that means showing how robots can be used as an adjunct to the assembly line or factory worker. The average manager knows he's going to have tremendous problems with organized labor if he or she starts tossing out people right and left and replacing them with robots. We have to take a gradual, soft-sell approach. Steer as clear of the labor question as you can; that's the client company's problem. Show how robots can be used in situations that are too dangerous for humans. Show how they can be used with humans to increase productivity. Use some examples of how robots are currently being used in the automobile industry—everyone knows how strong organized labor is there . . ."

"I've got it," Mike declared ruefully. He climbed to his feet and reached for the report. "I guess I got carried away with that seminar I took in Japanese business management. Trying to convert the world, I suppose."

"When you're being paid to sell robots to people who work under a different kind of system," Kali concluded with an understanding smile. "Think of it as a challenge!"

He grinned and swallowed the last of his coffee. "To the real world!" he said, lifting the empty cup in a small toast.

The real world. Kali watched him walk out the door and thought about her own real-world problems. Regardless of Lang Sterling's motives in seducing her, there was another, even more complex problem laying in wait at the back of her mind.

Why had she succumbed so easily to the seduction? She didn't want to admit it, but the knowledge was frightening. Never had she shown such a lack of control in a business situation! What had happened to her? There was no logical way to account for her actions. How had she come to find herself so attracted to a man with whom she had nothing in common, a man she was involved with only because she was trying to buy him for her company?

Restlessly she got to her feet, walking over to her window to stare broodingly down at the bustling Seattle traffic. What a fool she had been! What an untenable situation she had gotten herself into. What was she to do now? Turn the project of nailing Lang Sterling and his patents over to someone else in the firm?

She closed her eyes briefly against the thought of having to admit defeat. She had so wanted to pull off this particular coup. Even more so after she'd discovered Davis Wakefield's involvement . . .

The buzzing of her intercom pulled her attention away

from the street scene and she turned back toward her desk with a grimace.

"Yes, Joanna?"

"Mr. Sterling is on the line, Kali." Joanna's voice carried a note of congratulations. She was well aware of the effort her boss was spearheading to buy Lang Sterling and his patents.

If only Joanna knew the truth, Kali thought grimly as she stared at the intercom and considered not taking the call. A coward's way out, she chided herself. The man had to be dealt with sooner or later.

"Put him through."

"The next time I'm going to chain you to the foot of my bed," Lang growled laconically without any preamble as Kali picked up the receiver. "What the hell's the idea of sneaking off into the night like that? Get cold feet?"

"A lot of second thoughts which unfortunately came too late to do me much good!" she retorted unthinkingly.

"You're angry, aren't you?" he purred with evident satisfaction.

Kali reined in her shaky temper. She had to get control of herself and of the situation! "Not at you; at myself," she told him coldly.

"I figured that would be the case. You're the typical overresponsible, overachiever type who takes all the blame when things don't go according to plan," he opined cordially. "But look at the bright side: When things go right, you get to take the credit."

"What is that supposed to mean?" she demanded, frowning violently at the picture on the wall across from her desk. It was a scene of snow-capped Mount Rainier, the majestic, glacier-covered peak located about ninety-five miles from Seattle. She loved Mount Rainier but she hated that particular picture of it. It had belonged to Davis and one of these days she was going to toss it out.

101

"It means that if I decide to sell you the patents you'll be a heroine with your management and you'll have an opportunity to take a little revenge on that Wakefield character," he responded cheerfully.

Kali felt as if she were floundering in deep snow. Desperately she struggled to grasp the essentials of the matter. "Does that mean you've decided to accept IAI's offer?"

"I haven't really heard it yet, have I?" he pointed out smoothly. "When are you going to give me all the details?"

"Lang, I don't know what you're trying to do . . ."

"I thought it was obvious." He sounded surprised at her lack of intelligence. "I'm trying to arrange another opportunity to see you. I figure after last night you're probably too terrified to invite me over to dinner or accept another invitation to my place so I suggest we meet on neutral territory. A restaurant of your choosing." He paused significantly. "A place where we can talk business."

Stunned, Kali tried to think clearly. She simply hadn't been expecting this sort of approach from him. Was he using the lure of business to get her to see him again? Or was it that he had decided to talk business now that he felt he could handle Kali Havelock? Wheels within wheels . . .

"If you're serious about a business discussion," she began bravely.

"Oh, I am, I am."

"Then how about lunch at one of the places down on the wharf?" She kept her voice very even and brisk.

"It's dinner or nothing. And I'd rather eat at that little Continental place in Pioneer Square."

"I thought I was supposed to pick the time and the restaurant!" Kali bit out.

"Shall we say six thirty this evening? I'll pick you up."

"Lang, wait!" she called urgently into the phone, knowing she wasn't in a mood to face him again so soon. She needed time, as much of it as she could get. There were plans to make, assessments to perform. She was determined that this time she would handle matters properly . . . "I—I can't make it this evening."

There was a cold silence on the other end of the line and Kali tried to take some satisfaction in having set him back even a little.

"Why not?" he finally asked flatly.

"I'm . . . I'm going to be busy this evening. Business," she evaded purposefully.

"I see." She could almost hear him turning the subject over in his mind, trying to decide how much of an issue to make out of it. "In that case, tomorrow night it is," he stated coolly, and hung up the phone.

Kali put down the receiver trying to comprehend what was happening in her relationship with Lang Sterling. She stared unseeingly at the picture of Mount Rainier.

The answer was reached quickly enough by her agile mind. The reason she kept staring sightlessly at the wall was that, for what had to be one of the few times in her entire life, she didn't want to face the reality forced upon her by her own logic.

But there was no getting around it: Somehow Lang had reversed the roles in which Kali had cast both of them. Instead of being the clever, organized, and oh-so-wily huntress, Kali was beginning to feel like the hunted.

And after last night it was impossible to ignore the other side of the coin. Lang was becoming the hunter.

All of which was as confusing as it was alarming. The pencil Kali had been idly toying with suddenly snapped in half and she stared down at it in astonishment. This was ridiculous! She could handle stress better than this!

Furthermore she could handle men like Lang Sterling better than she had done so far, she told herself almost violently, getting to her feet. It was almost noon. What she needed was a brisk walk to clear her head and some of the strong French roast coffee at that little place near Pike Place Market! She had bought herself a little time before the next confrontation with Lang Sterling and she had better start using it to advantage.

Snatching up the khaki gabardine jacket she had worn into the office with the darker garbardine button-front skirt and khaki-toast blouse, Kali headed for the door.

"Joanna, I'll be back in about an hour," she announced in a matter-of-fact tone as she started past her secretary's desk. "Tell Mr. Renfrew I'll be ready with that presentation on marketing strategy this afternoon, will you? I know he's getting anxious . . ."

She broke off as Joanna responded to the phone on her desk. Her neat, graying head bent attentively over the receiver and then she cocked a brow upward in silent warning to her boss.

"One moment, Mr. Wakefield, I'll see if Miss Havelock is still in her office . . ." She stabbed the hold button and waited inquiringly for Kali's decision.

Kali's mouth curved in a wry little twist. "It's okay, Joanna, I'll speak to him. Didn't you get the good word? Hadley Industrial is in the running with us for Sterling!" She reached for the phone. Joanna had been Wakefield's secretary before he had left. Her loyalty had switched completely to the new vice-president and Kali never had been too certain but that part of the reason for that whole-hearted switch had been the news of how Davis had broken off the engagement.

"Hello, Davis, what can I do for you?" Kali glanced at the clock, hoping the conversation was not going to chew up too much of her lunch hour. She wanted the time away from the office to think . . .

"Kali," he began pleasantly enough, "I've got to hand

it to you. You seem to have Lang Sterling tied up in a neat bow and riding in your hip pocket!"

Kali frowned suspiciously. Was Davis really giving up this easily? After that relatively minor setback of getting himself kicked out of her apartment by Lang?

"Are you calling to congratulate IAI, then, Davis?" she tried smoothly.

"I'm calling to congratulate *you*, Kali. I've been trying to get hold of Sterling for two days and finally reached him a few minutes ago. The man claims he's more or less committed to sell the patents to you. Told me, in effect, to get lost," Davis added with a chuckle which was meant to imply he didn't worry about that sort of rudeness.

Kali, on the other hand, was experiencing a distinct sense of shock. Lang had told Davis he was committed to selling the patents to her? That didn't make any sense. If Davis had taken it upon himself to make another overture to Lang after that scene in the apartment it should have given the quarry the opportunity he needed to open negotiations without any risk to his pride. Why hadn't Lang taken advantage of that opening to try again for a bidding war between IAI and Hadley?

Still, whatever the reason, Kali wasn't going to miss her opportunity. "Well, that's business, Davis. Have a good trip back to Palo Alto and I'll send you advance sales information when IAI hits the market with its new products based on the Sterling patents!"

"Not so fast, honey," Davis murmured, and Kali instantly went on the alert. This was the man who had taught her almost everything she knew about surviving in the corporate world. He was smart, fast on his feet, and ruthless. And there was no reason to believe he'd taught her absolutely *everything* he knew! "I have a little proposition to make to you. One it would be well worth your time to consider . . ." The master to the apprentice . . .

105

Kali kept her tone perfectly level. "What proposition, Davis?" In spite of herself she was remembering that he had used a rather similar approach the day he had asked her to marry him. Davis Wakefield was all business. It was, literally, the most important thing in his life.

"A business proposition, honey. I'd like to discuss it with you at dinner. How about this evening? We could go to that Italian place we used to like so much over in Capitol Hill . . ."

"It's closed now, Davis," she cut in quietly. *Not to mention,* she added silently, *that I have no wish to go back to Capitol Hill this evening!*

"Any suggestions?"

"Davis, I don't see the point in all this. What is there to discuss?" she demanded crisply, aware of Joanna's slight frown.

"Money," he countered immediately. "A great deal of it. And a few other things which you might find very interesting, Kali," he added, his voice full of whatever meaning his listener might choose to hear. It was a trick he had, Kali remembered vaguely, that bit of letting an opponent get whatever wrong impression would do Davis the most good.

She thought for a moment, refusing to let him rush her. From a business standpoint there really was no reason to see Davis Wakefield again, but from a personal point of view the idea was intriguing. Something in her was attracted by the idea of showing the master how well the apprentice could handle herself now. He thought she had Lang Sterling in her hands, did he? Whatever the truth of the matter, she was more than delighted to know Davis believed her victorious in their small struggle. Could she resist the opportunity of confronting him in person with that victory? Whatever it was Davis wanted to discuss tonight, she was willing to bet it would be another attempt

106

to get Lang. How pleasant it would be to outmaneuver her mentor one more time . . .

"All right, Davis. I'll have dinner with you. There's a new place not far from my apartment . . ." She rattled off the address. "Seven o'clock?"

When he agreed without any hesitation, Kali hung up the phone with a bit of satisfaction. She felt as if she'd regained some of the momentum Lang had stripped from her when he'd coerced her into another meeting. This time, with Davis, at least, she felt back in charge of things!

But for the remainder of the afternoon and all during the time she was preparing for the confrontation with Davis that evening, one niggling doubt refused to be banished. What had Lang said to Wakefield to convince the other man Hadley Industrial Systems stood no chance of buying the patents? Furthermore, *why* would Lang cut Hadley out of the running? He had made it clear he wanted a bidding war for his services.

Deliberately she chose a soft, narrow, very understated dinner dress done in a muted wool stripe. She wanted just the right note of aloof power, she thought, rolling the hair along the side of her head and catching it in the back in a braid that was tucked under and held with a gold clip.

When she walked into the charming, intimate little restaurant three blocks from her apartment precisely at seven o'clock, Davis was waiting for her. She had to smile at the pains he had obviously taken with his own appearance. He was the picture of a well-dressed, conservative, successful businessman in his fine, gray pinstripe suit, polished leather shoes, and silk tie. The tawny brown hair was combed back in a neat, perfectly trimmed style.

But the hazel eyes were very cool as he came forward to greet her with his well-trained smile. Why hadn't she ever noticed how little emotion ever made it into that cold gaze, Kali wondered as she politely let him take her arm

107

and lead her toward the captain's desk. At least with Lang, came the unbidden thought, you were never in any doubt about his real mood! But, then, she supposed an inventor could afford to be far more honest about his emotions than a businessman.

No, it wasn't merely the difference in occupations which had bred that distinction in the two men, she decided intuitively. The difference lay in the fact that Lang Sterling was capable of genuine emotions, be they dangerous, passionate, or gentle. She shot a slanting glance at her escort as she abruptly acknowledged that Davis Wakefield would never be capable of such a range of feelings. For him everything was channeled toward whatever business goal happened to be in sight.

It might be possible for him to feel anger or frustration or satisfaction but they would always revolve around a very cold goal and hence lack the warm passion which came so easily to Lang.

And just where on this spectrum of passion, Kali thought, *do I fit?*

It was a jolting question and it took a surprising amount of effort to cover up the start it had given her. Nevertheless, Kali managed to handle the initial conversational pleasantries with a suitably light touch. Both she and Davis were fencing carefully, testing each other's guard.

"Do you miss Seattle, Davis?" she inquired politely as the cocktails were served. Her bland little smile was just the right touch to assure him she wasn't asking if he missed *her!*

"Not really," he countered easily, stirring his martini with the toothpick which held the olive. "Business is really alive down in California. The electronics industries are thriving and there's plenty of opportunity for someone with the drive and the will to make things happen." He nodded significantly. "It's the perfect environment for

108

someone like me, Kali. Or . . ." He smiled invitingly. "Someone like you."

She smiled right back, more blandly than ever. "Oh, I'm quite content here in Seattle." Now what the hell was he about? she wondered. She had the impression the pleasantries were ending and business was about to begin.

"I chose well when I chose you to train as my successor," he murmured. "You seem to have done very well for yourself at IAI."

"Are you waiting for me to thank you?" she asked coolly.

"No," he returned with an outwardly amused expression. "I'm about to see if you're interested in moving up in the world. You've certainly proven you can handle, the, er, exigencies of big business."

What was that supposed to mean? When in doubt, keep your mouth shut, Kali reminded herself. She sipped her drink and waited.

"Kali," he said, his expression sobering with that proper look of honest intent necessary when putting forth a business proposition, "Hadley Industrial is willing to pay well for talented people. Are you interested?"

Her lashes flickered as she absorbed the impact of his words. "Are you offering me a job, Davis?" she managed in a very soft voice.

"I can offer you another vice-presidency, Kali," he told her briskly. "A vice-presidency which carries a lot more clout than the one you have now. Hadley Industrial only has one vp slot, not several as IAI does. Furthermore, I can pay you a good deal more than what you're now earning, plus stock options in a company that's beginning to skyrocket."

"Fascinating," she returned dryly. "What's the catch?"

"Catch?" He looked innocently confused.

"Are you saying that after a year of working without me

you realize you need my brilliant management skills backing you up after all?" she mocked, her smoky eyes echoing the taunt in her voice.

"You're good, Kali. Why the hell do you think I singled you out at IAI? I can recognize talent when I see it. And now I'm in a position to pay for it."

"Davis," she murmured very clearly, inserting the proper amount of indulgent humor into her voice, "you didn't come to Seattle to find me; you came to get Lang Sterling. So why the pitch to me?"

He eyed her consideringly and then appeared to reach a decision. "Isn't it obvious? You've got Sterling. To get him, I am willing to pay for you, too."

"Ah," she breathed on a long whisper of comprehension. "Now we're getting down to the nitty-gritty. You are hoping to buy me on the assumption that I can bring Sterling along as part of the package."

"He's obviously not much of a businessman . . ." Davis began gruffly.

"Meaning he turned down the offer you made today?" she interpreted coolly. She still didn't understand what game Lang was playing in all this, but that could be worked out later. Right now she had to deal with Davis Wakefield.

"He wouldn't even listen to it." Davis smiled wryly. "What have you done to the man, Kali? I mean, besides seduce him?" he concluded a little too smoothly.

Kali felt the knife as he slipped it adroitly into place. She stifled the gasp of surging anger, keeping her voice even with an incredible effort. She could only be grateful the dim light in the restaurant concealed the flush of red fury which was seeking to stain her cheeks.

"I didn't seduce him, Davis," she told him flatly. "You know me as well as anyone. Would you say I'm the seductress type? I'm a cold, manipulating businesswoman, re-

110

member? The only romances I've ever been involved in were based on business. You should know that. Do you honestly see me as a femme fatale? Do you honestly believe I could set out to seduce a man and so blind him with passion that he would meekly turn over his patents and his soul to my firm?"

Davis eyed her narrowly, plainly trying to assess her mood. Kali wasn't surprised at his inability to categorize her current state of mind quickly. She was at a loss over the same issue. But something was driving her, something fierce and passionate and angry. She had *not* seduced Lang Sterling. That accusation wasn't really what was bothering her. What was enraging her was the knowledge that she couldn't have set out to seduce him even if she'd wanted to do so! What had actually happened was . . . was . . . inexplicable, damn it!

"He was in your apartment wearing only a towel the other morning, Kali," Davis reminded her grimly.

"I'd brought him home to talk business the night before. The man was drunk and passed out on my couch."

"The impression I had this morning was that he was *committed* to you, yet he didn't even know how much money IAI was prepared to offer. What was the basis of that commitment, Kali?" Davis charged, the gloves clearly off as he got down to the real business of the evening.

"Do you really believe I've captured him with my womanly wiles?" she taunted.

"Damn it, there's some reason he won't talk business with me!"

"Answer my question," she prodded coldly.

"I don't know what to believe," Davis flung back in cold frustration. "No, frankly, I don't see you managing to seduce the man. Knowing you as well as I do I believe it when you say you brought him back to your apartment with the intention of talking business. And I believe he probably did pass out on your couch! So what the hell kind of hold do you have on the man?"

Kali rose to her feet beside the booth in a swift, taut motion. There were glittering crystals of gray ice in her eyes as she smiled brittlely down at the baffled businessman.

"I don't have any hold on him, Davis. You see, I wasn't the one who did the seducing. You were quite right about that. *I was the one who got seduced!* And I'll tell you something else. Lang Sterling may happen to design robots for a living, but he certainly isn't one himself!"

Unable to think of anything else to add to the exit scene and fearing that her unruly emotions had already pushed her into saying far too much, Kali spun around and headed toward the door.

My God! she hissed silently to herself as she strode past the astonished maître d'. *What have I said? What have I done? Am I out of my mind?*

On the sidewalk outside she turned blindly toward her apartment building and began walking home, heedless of the chill night air moving in off Elliott Bay. Heedless, too, of the dangers of walking city streets alone at night, she made her way along the three blocks, her mind churning with a confusion she had never known.

That was definitely not how she'd intended to leave Davis Wakefield this evening! She had meant to do a little subtle one-upmanship, show the man she was every bit as ruthless and *professional* at her work as he was; that the apprentice, in fact, had outmaneuvered the master.

Instead she'd stormed out of the restaurant after grandly admitting to something which, in any rational light, could only be viewed as an incredible weakness! She had stood there and told Davis Wakefield she'd allowed herself to be seduced by the "rabbit" as if it were something of which to be proud!

112

Why hadn't she been suitably mysterious about her apparent "hold" on Lang Sterling? Wakefield had practically offered her a way of maintaining, even elaborating, her one-upmanship. She could have simply smiled cryptically and dropped a few hints of some vulnerability in Lang's past that she had discovered and was exploiting. Or she could have made it clear she'd snagged Lang by promising to top *any* offer Hadley made . . .

Her coppery nails bit into the leather of her purse as she walked the last block to the lobby of her building. Damn it! There were so many ways she could have handled the situation. She'd had Davis eating out of her palm. Imagine having him offer to take her on as a vice-president at Hadley if she'd bring Lang Sterling meekly in tow!

But no, she'd let herself become carried away by an emotion she didn't even fully understand. She'd given Davis Wakefield the impression she was the quarry, that it was Lang who had a hold on her!

Seething with the inability to comprehend her own reactions that evening, she rode the elevator up to her floor, exited into the carpeted hall, and fished for her key in the small purse she carried.

What woman in her right mind proudly announced she'd gotten herself seduced by the man she was supposed to be trapping in a business snare? And what had ever possessed her to throw Sterling's decidedly unrobotic behavior in Wakefield's face as if such behavior were somehow admirable or attractive?

Lang Sterling was hardly the kind of man she would have chosen to be seduced by if such choice was ever given a woman!

The man was totally incompatible with her.

The man ought to have been born into another world, a bygone century where the various hot-blooded masculine passions were more tolerated.

113

The man was unpredictable and, therefore, possibly dangerous. Furthermore, his unpredictability appeared to be contaminating her own actions. Therein lay a wholly unforeseen danger.

And the man was waiting for her in her apartment.

Kali's hand froze on the doorknob as his deep, gritty voice rasped her nerves. It emanated from the darkness of her living room.

"Where the hell have you been?"

CHAPTER SEVEN

"How did you get in here?"

Totally unnerved by the shock of finding Lang Sterling waiting like a coiled leopard in her darkened living room, Kali gasped out the first words which came to mind.

He came toward her, his leanness faintly illuminated by the pale light filtering in through the window behind him. His face, however, remained shadowed. Awkwardly Kali scratched for the light switch behind her and flipped it on.

"I thought you knew I'm good with mechanical things," he drawled laconically, coming to a halt a few paces away from her. "Robots, locks, you name it . . ."

"Lang! Stop looking at me like that and explain yourself!" Kali burst forth in an infuriated tone as she shut the door behind her with a small, furious little slam. "This is my apartment and I don't recall inviting you here this evening!"

His eyes narrowed and there was an implacable cast to his taut features. He was radiating the anger of a possessive, territorial male. Kali's instincts were alive to it even while her brain told her he had absolutely no right to be creating this scene.

Feet braced slightly, aggressively apart, Lang stood in a pair of faded, close-fitting jeans and regarded her with his hands on his hips in a classic stance of intimidating masculinity. The plaid, flannel shirt he wore was open at the collar and a few curls of coppery hair were just barely visible. Once again the roboticist didn't look at all as a roboticist ought to look, Kali thought fleetingly. Damn the man! Why couldn't he play his proper role in life?

"I came by to find out what your *business* was this evening," he told her tightly. "I thought I'd find you hiding here in your apartment, desperately trying to figure out how to handle me. I knew the bit about being unavailable because of business was an excuse but I sure as hell didn't think you'd have the gall to be out on a date!"

"Gall! If we're going to talk about sheer gall," Kali began, tossing her purse down onto a chair and using the small action as a way of stalking out of his reach, "let's discuss yours! This amounts to breaking and entering, you know!" She flung out a hand to indicate his presence in her apartment. "Furthermore, I *was* out on business, although I don't know why I should be bothered with defending myself to you! You're the one who should be coming up with an explanation and an apology!"

"What other explanation is called for, under the circumstances?" he snapped, shifting his weight slightly to follow her movement across the room.

"*What* circumstances?"

"Last night!"

Kali felt her breath catch in her throat. "Last night," she repeated, dumbfounded. "What's last night got to do with anything?"

It was the wrong thing to say; she realized that almost instantly. Instead of following her progress across the

116

room with a glittering green gaze, Lang began closing in on her. A chill flashed up her spine even as she instructed herself not to let him unnerve her. The low, gritty threat in his voice when he spoke again was one more element to assimilate and deal with at the end of what had been an extremely difficult day for Kali.

"Don't play the cool, calculating little robot with me, Kali Havelock. I know you too well now. *Last night* taught me too much. That's one of the reasons it was very important to us. Shall I tell you what else happened *last night?*"

"Lang, stop it this instant! You have no right . . . !"

"Rights," he repeated with a short, grim nod. "Yes, that's the next item of importance on the list of things which happened last night! You gave me all sorts of rights last night . . ."

He was getting much too close. The slow, cat-lazy stalk was pushing her back toward the huge windows and try as she might, Kali couldn't bring herself to stand her ground just yet. She was still trying to work out the best approach to handling this intruder in her apartment who was acting out the role of the heavy-handed lover laying down the law. No, she corrected herself a little hysterically, Lang wasn't acting out the role; he was living it as if it were second nature!

"Don't be ridiculous! Just because we—we somehow wound up in bed together, that doesn't mean . . ."

"Oh, no you don't, you little coward! You're not going to get away with pretending that what happened in my bed was some sort of casual, unexpected interlude which didn't have any strings attached! You didn't wind up there by accident! I carried you off to bed and I made very deliberate love to you there! Furthermore, you gave yourself to me and don't you dare deny it. You're mine now,

117

Kali, and if you think I'm going to let you get away with seeing other men, you're out of your head!"

"I wasn't seeing another man! I mean, I was, but it was business. Damn it, look how early it is. If I'd been out on a hot date do you think I'd be home at this hour?" Kali ground her teeth in frustration. "Why in hell am I explaining myself to you? I've got a right to spend my evenings as I please! Lang, you're upsetting me and I don't appreciate it one bit. Will you kindly stop behaving as if you stepped through some time warp in the past? This is the twentieth century, although you seem to have trouble understanding that! You don't own me just because you—you slept with me last night!"

"Who was he?" Lang rapped out, totally ignoring her desperate little lecture.

Kali backed yet another step, torn between rage and genuine feminine fear. He closed the small gap she had created, not touching her but well within reach now.

"I've told you I was involved in a business discussion!" Her back to the cold glass, Kali drew herself up very straight, her chin lifting boldly. She would not tolerate this sort of behavior any longer!

"Who was he?" Lang repeated the question, not raising his voice but somehow infusing it with a new level of menace.

"Davis Wakefield! Now will you please stop acting the jealous lover? I *told* you it was business!"

"Wakefield! What the hell did he want?"

The answer didn't appear to have satisfied him in the least. Kali was abruptly furious with herself for compromising to such an extent.

"What do you think he wanted? It certainly wasn't *me* he was after, although he was willing to pay a handsome price for what he seems to think I can deliver!"

"Me?" Lang hazarded coolly.

118

"Who else? You're the only reason Davis is in town and if you'll make some attempt to control your interesting if not precisely amusing display of male idiocy, you might possibly remember that!"

Lang considered his victim, who glared back. Then he tipped his head to one side and asked on a surprisingly curious note, "How much?"

"What?" Kali stared at him blankly.

"How much was he willing to pay you for delivering me?"

"Does this slight change of topic mean you're through badgering me about where I've been this evening?" she shot back icily.

He shrugged but didn't move, thereby keeping her effectively pinned against the glass. "I am kind of curious," he drawled. "Always interesting to know what one would bring on the open market."

Kali frowned. "I thought you wanted to be on the open market. You said you wanted to start a bidding war between Hadley and IAI. Lang, why in the world did you lead him to think I had some sort of special hold over you? Davis thinks I've got you in the palm of my hand! That I can do anything I want with you!"

The bronze-green eyes gleamed faintly with what might have been a trace of amusement. "I didn't go that far. I merely told him I was committed to you and if you wanted to buy the patents, they were yours."

"But why?" she pleaded. "Lang, I don't understand!"

"Because of last night, of course," he murmured softly. "Actually, to be perfectly honest, I suppose I had already made the decision the night I let you talk me down off that staircase."

"Are you out of your mind?" she gasped, totally at a loss to comprehend this erratic male. "You were furious the next morning when you thought I'd deliberately made

119

things awkward between you and Hadley Industrial by letting you create a scene!"

"Well, I don't take too kindly to being manipulated," Lang agreed consideringly. "And you *had* manipulated me that morning. You knew damn well how I'd react emerging from the shower to find you entertaining another man!"

Kali said nothing, watching him from under lowered lashes. It was the truth but there was no need to push the issue.

Lang put out a hand, sliding his strong, sensitive fingers around her neck and tugging gently. When she resisted mutely, for a moment his mouth crooked wryly but he didn't force her closer.

"You seem to know me very well in some ways," he went on in a low, velvety voice. "But in others you're incredibly blind. You're not going to do a really first-class job of manipulating me until you learn more about me . . ."

She eyed him warily, feeling the sensual tension curling around them, drawing them closer. Lang's fingers on her nape moved in a slow, coaxing motion, stirring the primitively electric nerves there.

"I haven't been trying to manipulate you, Lang. I was trying to do business with you . . ."

"There's no business left to do," he returned. "If you'd gone out with me tonight instead of Wakefield, you'd have known the business end of things is all signed, sealed, and delivered. Must have been something of a shock hearing the news from Wakefield first, hmmm?"

"Lang, this doesn't make any sense," she heard herself wail softly. "IAI will make you a terrific deal, of course," she went on hurriedly, "but you haven't even heard our deal yet. Why should you be agreeing to it without bothering to discuss it?"

"I keep telling you. Because of last night," he growled, exerting just enough pressure on her nape to draw her a step closer.

"But the only thing that happened last night was that . . ." Kali broke off and searched for the right words. They didn't exist. "The only thing that happened last night was that you seduced me!" she exploded softly.

A slow, highwayman's grin slashed across Lang's features and the near-green eyes gleamed more brightly. "Did you tell Wakefield that?"

Kali gritted her teeth. "Don't remind me!"

He chuckled, a chuckle that went very well with the amused, buccaneering expression. "I'd like to have heard that! Did you tell him before or after he'd tried to buy me by purchasing you?"

"It's none of your business! Damn it, Lang, I don't understand what you're playing at . . ."

"That's your whole problem," he soothed, forcing her a little closer. She was only inches away from him now, fully alive to the heat of his hard body and the high-strung sensations seeping along her nerves. What was the matter with her? She was not the high-strung type. She'd never been the high-strung type. Why did this man seem able to provoke a restless unease in her just by touching her?

"What's my whole problem?" she grated as he wrapped his other arm around her waist and pulled her the remainder of the short distance.

"You think I'm playing at something and I'm not. We weren't playing last night, Kali. We made love last night. You gave yourself to me . . ."

"No!"

"And I committed myself to you," he concluded as if she hadn't interrupted. He met her eyes as she raised her face to gaze up at him a little desperately.

"Lang, please! It was only a night we had together. I

121

should never have let you talk me into bed in the first place. I don't know what I was thinking to allow such a thing to happen!"

"You weren't thinking. You were reacting. All traces of the little robot in you were put on hold last night. You were all woman in my arms. And I didn't talk you into bed," he added with a quirking smile, "I carried you off to bed. The same way I'm going to do tonight!"

"No! Damn it, I won't . . . !"

Her words were sealed behind her lips as he ignored her protest and captured her mouth with his own.

A shudder went through her from head to toe as Kali stood very still beneath the sensuous onslaught. Her fingers splayed across his chest and her eyes were tightly shut. His kiss seemed to act like a powerful drug on her nervous system, sapping her will and beguiling her in a way no other man's had ever succeeded in doing.

Lang Sterling's enthralling embraces made those of any other man Kali had ever known seem robotic in comparison. It was as if she had been existing in a world of superficial, manipulating, intelligent machines and had adapted herself to survive in such an environment. She had adapted so well that it came as a shock to discover she wasn't really like that herself.

But all her skills and training had been in the world of corporate robots and this pre-twentieth-century male with his potent, overwhelmingly romantic approach to life seemed to have no problem at all in ignoring her defenses.

Kali tried to put up the barriers, only to find each one more useless than the last. The excitement Lang generated was too tempting, his masculine lures were too magical. How could a modern, level-headed, corporate woman fight a man who waged war under the passionate, romantic rules of another era? An era which might not even have existed except in his head?

"Lang, you're not going to do this to me again," she managed thickly as he released her mouth to nuzzle the delicate spot behind her ear.

"Do what to you again?" he teased roughly, twining his fingers in the neat braid and beginning to unwrap it. "Seduce you and carry you off to bed? Of course I am. Why do you think I bothered coming here tonight in the first place?"

She struggled fiercely for a moment, thoroughly annoyed with his words. "Of all the egotistical, chauvinistic statements! Lang Sterling, what makes you think you can barge in here and haul me off to bed?"

"It seems a fair enough exchange," he purred, using the tip of his tongue to circle the interior of her ear. The erotic caress sent another wave of tremors through her which she couldn't suppress.

"Exchange for what!" Kali hissed. She tried to draw her head out of reach but he put up a hand and forced her gently down onto his shoulder.

"For the fact that you've got me tied up hand and foot." He laughed huskily, nipping sharply at her earlobe. "Wakefield was right, Kali. The patents are yours. Anything I have is yours. I'm completely at your mercy, sweetheart. How could I possibly outmaneuver a shrewd little businesswoman like yourself?"

"But I haven't . . . I didn't get a chance to even go over the deal with you!"

"Details. We'll get to them sooner or later. I'd give you those patents for free, you know, but it would be nice to get enough to get myself out of hock."

"Will you please be serious, Lang? We have to talk!"

"Not unless you've got something important to talk about and so far you haven't said anything we want to hear tonight . . ."

He bent his head to her anxious mouth and shaped the

outline of her lips with his tongue. Kali heard herself moan deep in her throat. The next thing she was aware of was the probing, prying pressure of his thumb at the corner of her mouth.

"Oh, Lang . . ."

Her lips parted on a sigh of surrender and he moved to consolidate his gain, plunging hungrily into the warm territory behind her teeth. With his fist coiled ruthlessly in her hair, Lang drank his fill of the warm honey he found in her mouth, exploring every sensitive, hidden place and then seeking out her tongue in a thrilling battle.

Breathless and trembling, Kali continued to give ground before the deeply romantic assault. She could not summon any genuine willpower to stop it. It was as if some part of her had been looking for this all her life. Her fingertips stopped digging into the flannel of his shirt and sought the muscles of his shoulders instead. The feel of the hard contours was unbelievably intriguing and Kali pressed closer of her own accord.

His mouth fastened on hers, Lang let his hands glide down the length of her back in a slow, molding touch that connected them from breast to thigh. When he reached her hips he curled his fingers around the curving shape of her and forced her deeply into his straining body.

He wanted her, Kali thought on a note of wonder, just as he had wanted her last night. He was completely honest about the attraction he felt. She found it almost impossible to believe he would throw business caution to the winds for the sake of an affair with her, of all people, but that seemed to be what he was doing.

Under the impetus of her own rising excitement and desire, Kali freed her mouth to find the line of his tanned throat. She felt him tremble as she strung small kisses down to where the collar of the flannel shirt was caught by a button. When he groaned, his lips in her hair, Kali cautiously undid the button and pressed her lips to the hair-roughened skin of his chest.

As if the small caress was more than he could tolerate, Lang lifted one arm, cradling her head and tilting it back. Then he was the one seeking the vulnerable points along the line of her throat. As he traced a fiery path down to the pulse point, he used his free hand to open the buttons of her soft, striped wool dress. Kali gasped when he found the upper curves of her small breasts with his lips and her fingers clung savagely in the thick red-brown hair as she held him close.

"Oh, Lang . . ."

"In my arms you're not a little business robot, are you, sweetheart?" he muttered hoarsely as he freed the front snap of her bra. "I love the way you come alive with passion. It's like setting free something wild and then taming it to my hand . . ."

Kali lifted her heavy lashes at his words. "And what do I do to you, Lang?" she whispered.

He feathered the peak of one breast with his tongue and then raised his head to meet her eyes. "Isn't it obvious? I'm as much your captive as you are mine. The chains I hold you with also bind me. It's like riding the tiger. Once started, there's no safe way to get off!"

For an instant longer their glances meshed and held and then, with a lithe, powerful movement, Lang swept her up into his arms and started toward the bedroom.

From out of nowhere Kali summoned up one last objection:

"Lang, wait, I'm not . . . I mean I haven't anything with which to protect myself tonight . . ." She stumbled over the words, remembering all too well that last night she had been so swept off her feet she hadn't even thought about such commonsense things as birth control!

He smiled down at her. "I said I came here tonight with

125

every intention of seducing you and carrying you off to bed, honey. That means I came *prepared* to seduce you and carry you off to bed. Relax, darling," he went on reassuringly as he strode through the door of her bedroom. "I'll take care of you."

There didn't seem to be anything left to say. Helpless in the grip of her rising passion, Kali looked up at him as he set her gently on her feet and reached down to turn back the covers of the bed. Then he stood gazing into her eyes for a long moment, his fingers playing lightly, tantalizingly in her hair. Finally he slipped off her glasses.

Slowly he lowered his head and sought out her mouth as he slid the remainder of her garments off her body. When she stood naked and trembling with her longing he cupped her breasts in his hands and drew excruciatingly exciting circles around the hardening nipples.

In response, Kali locked her fingers behind his head and arched backward slightly, urging him to put his lips where his fingers now were.

He obeyed with the willingness of a man who found the evidence of her arousal a fiercely arousing thing in itself. Kali thought she would lose her balance as the strength seemed to go from her limbs. She clung more tightly as he grazed the tips of her aching, throbbing breasts first with his tongue and then with his teeth.

"Oh, Lang . . ."

The small stinging of his teeth set off a new wave of fire along her nerve endings and she knew he must have felt it. When the hardness of her nipples appeared to satisfy him at last, Lang sank lower, going down on one knee as his hands glided along her rib cage to the thrust of her thigh.

Across the warm, silky skin of her stomach his mouth rained more damp fire as he clenched the fullness of her hips with gentle violence. Kali whispered his name softly, achingly, her fingers massaging the smoothly muscled shoulders and the strong column of his neck.

When his tongue dipped into the small depression in the center of her stomach, she instinctively sucked in her breath, and then he was using his fingers to trace exotic patterns along the outside of her thighs.

"Kali, my sweet, passionate lover . . ." he rasped as the tracing fingers moved slowly, thrillingly to the inside of her legs. "How could you not realize last night that you were mine now? There's no going back . . ."

His sensitive hand probed the joining of her thighs with a tantalizing caress and Kali's breath caught in her throat. Unable to help herself she arched closer to the magic of his touch. What he did to her was beyond all understanding. He made her want to give herself completely in a way that transcended the physical. She felt at once wanton and wise, submissive and utterly demanding.

"I love the feel of your warmth," he growled against the skin of her stomach as he started a dancing pattern on the most delicate and sensitive portion of her body. "Soft and welcoming . . . I got lost in your softness last night, sweet Kali. I can't wait any longer to get lost again . . ."

Straightening slowly, dropping hungry little kisses along the way until his mouth nipped excitingly at the skin of her shoulder, Lang lifted her once more and settled her between the white sheets.

Kali watched him from beneath heavy lids as he undressed. A curling rope of passion was churning inside her, fed by the sight of him as he shrugged out of the plaid shirt and unclasped his belt. The coppery hairs tapering down his chest were an irresistible temptation and she propped herself shakily up in bed, extending one hand to touch the fire.

His hands paused in the act of undoing the belt buckle and she felt him shiver as she touched him.

"Finish undressing me, Kali," he begged huskily, eyes very green with his pleas.

"Yes," she whispered, curling her legs beneath her. Kneeling on the bed she slowly unzipped the jeans and began pushing them down his narrow hips.

When he stepped out of them her hands went to the waistband of his briefs. She fumbled as she pushed them aside, revealing the surging strength of his manhood.

In that moment Kali was assailed by a sudden shyness. It was easier, she realized dimly, when he was the one making love to her. She could close her eyes and surrender to the pleasures of his hands and his lips.

As if he sensed her hesitation to commit herself by taking the lead in the lovemaking, Lang caught his hands deeply in the tangle of her jungle-cat–colored hair and pulled her close to him.

"You want me," he whispered throatily. "Show me you want me!"

Her lips were on the skin of his chest as he held her to him and the scent of his aroused body was unbelievably exhilarating. The need to please and be pleased drove out the moment of uncertainty she had experienced and Kali wrapped her arms around his waist, kissing the roughness of his chest and stomach.

She heard him suck in air and felt the hard, passionate strength of his body. Her senses began to revel in being able to arouse him so and her hands pressed against the base of his spine, arching him closer. Then, unable to resist any longer, she drew her fingers around his waist and gently caught the thrusting maleness of him. Slowly, tenderly, her gilded nails wove intimate designs on his body.

Designs, she realized somewhere in the haze of her passion, which seemed to drive him over some impossible edge.

"Kali!"

He pushed her heavily back against the white sheet and her hair fanned out on the pillow as she watched him fumble hurriedly with the pocket of his jeans. She was glad one of them was capable of some rational thought. A moment later he came down on top of her with unleashed desire.

"My God, Kali, I'm half out of my mind over you, don't you know that?"

"Lang, oh, Lang . . . !"

Her body arched upward against his strength and he captured the lifting feminine hips in his hands, anchoring her for a second while his legs sought a place between hers.

As if the demand in him were an invitation to an ancient battle, Kali held her legs tightly together for a moment, refusing him the admittance he now seemed to assume was his by right. She felt him go momentarily very still and opened her eyes to find him staring down into her face. Her lips parted challengingly and the smoke in her gaze was a mysterious cloud from behind which emanated a siren's call.

"You're a witch, sweetheart," he growled, green eyes glittering above the taut lines of his face. "And witches get burned . . ."

"Yes," she agreed, taunting him with her body as she ran her nails lightly across his back. God! She felt like a witch or a siren or a provoking lover . . . not at all like a robot!

"Then we'll both go up in flames," he vowed, and came back down on her with the full force of his superior strength.

"Oh!"

Her cry was torn from her half-blocked throat as he eased his knee between her thighs and found the path he sought. His mouth fastened on hers as he drove against her body, making them one in a shock of power.

129

Kali's small attempt at teasing him collapsed as she surrendered totally to the consuming fire that blazed between them. Her legs wrapped around him as he swept her close. She gave herself up to the rhythm of his lovemaking, letting it carry her along even as he seemed to be carried along by the same spiraling excitement.

The waves rolled through them and over them until neither could have told where one body stopped and the other began. Kali felt simultaneously worshipped, tenderly held, violently captured. It was a dizzying combination of sensations that took away her breath and left her longing only for more of the man above her.

When the tightening thread of passion reached the point of no return and snapped, Kali shuddered in Lang's grasp, crying out his name even as he went rigid a few seconds later. For a moment they both hovered, suspended in the net of releasing energy, and the world around them ceased to exist.

It was a long time later that Kali stirred and drifted slowly back to her senses under the impetus of a teasing, provoking pattern being lazily drawn on the damp skin of her breast.

Her eyes fluttered open to find Lang smiling down at her with the satisfaction of a thoroughly contented male. The pattern on her skin was being carried out by the fingers of his left hand as he propped himself on his right elbow.

For a moment their eyes met and then Lang bent to drop a tiny kiss on her nose.

"You never did tell me how much Wakefield offered you."

She wrinkled her freshly kissed nose at him, trying to pull her lazy thoughts back in order. "A vice-presidency with more power and a whole lot more money."

"Sounds tempting. Were you?" he murmured dryly.

"Was I what?" She really didn't want to think about Davis right now.

"Were you tempted?"

"No!"

"I didn't think you would be." Lang chuckled. "Did you enjoy your little moment of revenge?"

She shut her eyes on a groan of memory. "I misplayed the scene entirely," Kali admitted. "He wanted to know what hold I had on you and I wound up telling him I didn't have any hold at all! That you were the one who had seduced me, not vice versa."

His soft, pleased laughter forced her eyes back open and she glared up at him reproachfully.

"You little idiot," he mused, shaking his head in slow wonder. "Don't you realize yet that what we have is mutual? Whatever hold I have on you is only equaled by the one you have on me!"

She gnawed on her rather bruised lip, trying to understand the situation, but it seemed beyond her. "You're . . . you're willing to turn your patents over to my firm just because you want me?" she breathed disbelievingly.

"Can you think of a better reason?" He chuckled, smoothing the hair gently away from her face.

"But, Lang! That's not . . . that's not good *business!*" she gasped.

"I'm really not into business," he told her gravely. "There are other things in this world which interest me more."

"Lang, this is ridiculous." Kali struggled to a sitting position against the pillows, automatically clutching at the sheet and pulling it up to cover herself. Her brows came together in a severe frown. "You've got to think about your future!"

"My future is with you," he said simply.

"But you can't know that for sure!" she protested.

"I knew it after last night. I keep telling you, Kali, last night was very important." His mouth lifted in soft humor but he watched her now with a hint of wariness in his eyes.

Dazedly Kali forced her beleaguered brain back into action. With increasing willpower she tried to untangle the threads of the situation, assessing, analyzing, computing . . .

"What if I just . . . take the patents and run, so to speak?" she challenged him coolly.

"You won't." He sounded firm.

"What's to stop me?"

His gaze seemed to soften in what might have been an almost wistful manner. "There's a small catch attached to this little arrangement."

"I knew it! What catch?"

"You have to marry me in order to get the patents."

Kali stared at him blankly for a startled instant. *"Marry you!"*

He said nothing, merely watching her through wary, cautious eyes.

And Kali couldn't help herself. She blinked at this stranger from the past who had made himself her lover and then she collapsed, laughing, against the pillows.

CHAPTER EIGHT

"What's the matter, Kali?" Lang growled as he watched her scrabble for her glasses on the nightstand and push them onto her nose. "Can't you handle that kind of commitment?"

Kali, trying to control the slowly subsiding fit of chuckles, shook her head and leaned back onto the pillows again. She peered at him through the lenses of her glasses and thought about men who had accidentally been born into the wrong century. Just her luck, she told herself ruefully, to have gotten herself involved with one! Imagine a man trying to force a woman to marry him in this day and age! Imagine a man wanting a woman that badly . . .

No, she didn't want to pursue that line of thought, she realized immediately. Besides, Lang couldn't be serious! Even he couldn't be that old-fashioned and . . . and impossibly romantic!

Everyone was out for something. Lang wanted a good deal for his patents and his brains. He had tried to create a bidding war between IAI and Hadley and then had abandoned the notion after the encounter with Davis. Now he must be trying another tactic.

Did he think that by seducing her he was going to ensure the best possible deal with Interactive Automation, Inc.?

No, that didn't quite make sense either, knowing what she did about Lang's peculiarly non–twentieth-century personality. He *was* the kind of man to call another man out at dawn or carry a woman off into the night or . . . or try and force a woman he wanted into marriage.

Nothing like spiraling confusion to erase all traces of amusement, Kali decided as the last of the laughter faded in her. What was going on here?

"You," she announced with grand certainty, "can't possibly be serious."

"You're the one who isn't ready to be serious," he countered quietly, studying her intently. "So we'll try something you can handle without going off into gales of laughter."

Kali arched a brow, fighting to maintain a calm, aloofly amused expression. It was difficult, given the resolute determination in those bronze-green eyes. She had to be careful, she thought grimly. It would be disastrous if she allowed herself to be dragged back through the same time warp Lang Sterling used. She knew full well in which century she belonged!

"I didn't think you had gone *that* crazy," she noted, and didn't bother to ask herself why she felt a little sad about the fact. "So what's your next best offer?"

He stood up without answering her and disappeared into the bathroom. Kali sat frowning at the closed door, listening to the sound of running water and wondering what was going on in his increasingly hard-to-understand brain.

When he emerged a few minutes later she lifted her

chin, waiting for him to continue where he had left off. But he didn't. Instead, he threw her a small, intimate smile and walked out the door and down the hall.

Kali stared blankly at the empty doorway, listening as he rummaged around in her kitchen. What was he up to now? Uneasily she stirred beneath her sheet. She was about to swing her feet off the bed and march down the hall after him when he reappeared in the doorway.

She glared at him warily as he came toward her, unabashedly naked and carrying a bottle of champagne and two glasses.

"What in the world . . . ?"

"Good"—he nodded, sitting down beside her on the bed and pouring the champagne—"at least you're no longer laughing." He handed her a glass and raised his own in a small toast. "To us."

"What about us?" Kali held the champagne glass gingerly, aware of her increasing apprehension.

He sipped his bubbling drink and met her eyes over the rim of the glass.

"Our new, twentieth-century–style relationship," he explained in a laconic drawl.

"Lang, if you don't tell me what's going on, so help me, I'll . . . !"

"You're coming to live with me in exchange for those patents," he interrupted coolly, downing another swallow of the champagne.

"Live with you!" she yelped. The liquid in her glass nearly slopped over the edge. Hastily she steadied it, her attention torn between worrying about spilling the champagne and frowning furiously at the man who sat so calmly on the edge of her bed.

"For a month," he clarified. "You can comprehend that, can't you? A month of living with me in exchange for turning those patents over to IAI. That doesn't mean

135

I don't expect a sound deal out of IAI, you realize," he added blandly. "It just means you're part of that deal. In addition to the money, I want you in my bed for a month."

Kali froze as the wave of angry red stained her skin from her breasts to her cheeks. "You can't do this!"

He considered her thoughtfully. "I see you're beginning to take me seriously. You didn't believe me when I said I wanted marriage, did you?"

"Well, no, of course not!" she snapped, confused and angry. The glass of champagne in her hand, which needed constant attention so as not to spill, and her nakedness beneath the flimsy sheet left her feeling incredibly vulnerable. The fact that Lang was naked without even the protection of a sheet and was also balancing a glass of champagne didn't seem to even up the situation at all. He wore the cloak of masculine assurance and satisfaction which came to a man who has just made successful love to a woman and knows that he's in control.

"So why are you taking me seriously now when I've changed my demands?" he prodded interestedly.

"Lang, are you teasing me?" she charged tightly.

"Nope. I just find it interesting that you laughed at the idea of marriage but you're looking downright terrified I might really force you to come and live with me."

Kali's eyes went very cloudy with the impact of the confusion and inexplicable fear assailing her. "Are you going to force me to come and live with you?" she whispered.

"It won't exactly be force, will it? You're already halfway there, Kali Havelock. This is the second night we've spent in bed together and there will be a lot more in the future. We both know that. We've both admitted we're more than mildly attracted to each other!" he concluded on a small laugh. "Don't forget you admitted to your ex-fiancé tonight that I'd seduced you. If you like I'll go out and tell the rest of the city I can't resist *you*. But there's no need, is there?"

"You think that because I've . . . I've gone to bed with you a couple of times, you can stretch that out into a month-long affair?" she blazed.

"Yes," he said simply. "With or without the patents thrown into the bargain. Face it, Kali, you're going to have an affair with me. Might as well secure the business side of the deal at the same time."

"And if I refuse?" she demanded tautly.

"Then I'll take the patents elsewhere. But I don't think you're going to refuse, are you, sweetheart?" He reached out and tipped the champagne glass to her lips, forcing her to take a long swallow. Then he removed it from her nerveless fingers and placed it on the bedside table along with his own.

Next he took off her glasses and leaned over her, bracing his hands on either side of her hips. "If you don't move in with me, I'll move in with you. It doesn't really matter very much. But one way or another we're going to be together for a month. It's the price I'm putting on those patents and you're going to pay it because you can't resist me."

Before she could summon an angry protest or find a rational way of handling the situation, Kali was being crushed back into the pillows beneath Lang's heavy, drugging kiss.

In the morning, she told herself dimly as the waves of passion swept through her once more, in the morning she would find a logical way out of the trap Lang had built for her. Of course she could outthink and outmaneuver a man who thought in eighteenth-century terms!

But in the meantime the temptation to suspend the rational side of her nature and let the whirlpool take her was too great. She parted her lips beneath his with a small

137

moan which he swallowed and her arms came around the sleek, strong back with a hunger she could never have rationalized.

It wasn't until nine o'clock the next morning when she was summoned to the office of her boss, the chief executive officer of Interactive Automation, Inc., that Kali finally began to force herself to think properly. She sat facing Maxwell Spencer, her features composed and serenely alert in the approved manner, and desperately struggled to pull herself together.

It had been an upsetting morning, to say the least. She had awakened to find Lang gone and a note left on her dresser. The message, written in a huge, curly scrawl, reminded her simply of their date that evening and the deal they had made. In that order. It was signed with an oversized L.

Kali had torn up the note in a furious little gesture and slammed her way out of the apartment. It wasn't until the familiar, controlled surroundings of her workplace embraced her that she finally managed to get a grip on her spinning, chaotic emotions. The summons to Spencer's office had come just as she was recovering over a cup of coffee.

"Just wanted to check with you on the status of our latest acquisition." Max Spencer smiled easily.

Kali smiled back with the cool self-assurance necessary for a vice-president of IAI. It struck her that after all these months she still didn't know her boss very well. She had been so careful to keep an almost formal distance between them while she proved herself. Spencer was a large man, nearing fifty but with still-firm features. His gray hair was thick and well styled, his suit hand-tailored and expensive. He was a success but Kali had the impression he had become a success on his own terms.

"You mean Lang Sterling and his patents?" Internally

she stilled the strange panic she was experiencing. "I think everything should be all tied up by the end of the week," she went on to offer carefully.

"Good, good." Max nodded, appearing pleased. "I understand he's a bit eccentric?"

"Very," she agreed feelingly.

"That's presenting a problem?" Max pressed keenly.

"I'm dealing with it," she murmured, trying to sound in charge of the situation.

Max eyed her assessingly. "This will be a nice little coup for you and IAI, Kali. With access to the technology implicit in those patents and with Sterling's inventive abilities available to us, IAI will make a clean sweep of the market."

"Until someone else catches up with another jump on technology," she reminded him. "Nothing stands still, Max, and in this business there are a lot of people working on the next breakthrough. It's only a matter of time . . ."

He waved her to silence. "I'm aware of the competitive element in the business." He smiled grimly. "But there's no doubt Sterling will give us one hell of an edge. Keep me in touch with the situation as it develops, will you? Does he seem satisfied with the package we're offering?"

"He's, uh, made a couple of modifications," she got out, controlling her body's urge to blush with an almost superhuman effort.

"Well, we expected that." Max nodded comfortably.

"Yes," she agreed weakly.

"Right. Well, I'll check with you later on this week, then. Thanks for dropping by, Kali." Her boss nodded his dismissal and Kali obediently arose and moved gratefully to the door with a feeling of rising hysteria.

Things were getting complicated.

But she could handle them, she told herself resolutely.

She made that statement on and off for the rest of the day. But by the time she returned home to dress for her date with Lang the little darts of panic were coming with increasing frequency.

She was beginning to feel trapped, she realized as she selected the black silk sheath which was cuffed and hemmed with a splurge of crisp white lace. She had committed herself to her boss and she was on the edge of another, far deeper commitment to Lang Sterling.

Surely she could still do something about the latter commitment, she thought frantically as she braided her hair and curled it in a sophisticated knot on her nape. Her career came first, not some wild, unfathomable reaction to a man with whom she had virtually nothing in common!

But how was she going to separate the two now that Lang had bound both commitments together by the simple act of making her part of the deal for the patents?

A month with him . . .

He was right, she forced herself to admit with grave honesty as she met her own eyes in the mirror. She was already involved in an affair with him. And she wasn't at all sure she could call a halt as long as he was intent on carrying her off to bed! Look at what had happened the past two nights. Look what an idiot she'd made of herself by telling Davis her quarry had seduced her! Look at how obediently she was dressing for dinner with Lang this evening!

Kali turned away from the mirror in wry disgust and searched for the black pumps she wanted to wear with the dress. The intercom chimed as she straightened.

Lang announced himself in a short, gritty word and with a feeling of foreboding, Kali pressed the downstairs door release. She awaited his arrival at her front door as if she were awaiting the hand of fate.

But when she opened the door, it wasn't fate that was pushed into her hands, it was a bouquet of yellow roses.

"Oh, Lang! They're beautiful!"

He smiled at the splash of yellow against her black silk dress as she bent over the flowers. "I thought they'd go with the room," he explained modestly, stepping over the threshold and capturing her chin lightly for a swift, possessive kiss that left her mouth feeling softened. "And with you."

For an instant their eyes clung and Kali had to break the spell with a surge of sheer willpower. Taking a breath, she deliberately stepped out of reach and hurried off to the kitchen to find a bowl. Damn the man! He had a knack for disarming her. She'd steeled herself to confront him this evening and he'd thrown her off stride with the simple gesture of handing her a bunch of flowers!

But business was business and she was going to have to wind up this sticky situation, she instructed herself firmly as she arranged the roses. Surreptitiously she watched Lang casually help himself to a small glass of Scotch and stroll over to the window. He was wearing a perfectly fitted brown jacket with a subtle stripe woven in, a darker pair of trousers, and a cream-colored shirt. The tie was brown with a gold design. In the soft living room light the deep russet hair gleamed as he stood sipping the Scotch and staring out into the night.

Kali's hand froze in the act of placing a yellow rose and she realized she was staring at Lang's hard profile. What was it about this man that made her so weak?

She shut her eyes briefly. She'd fallen victim to a fleeting sexual attraction. That's what it was. There was no other logical explanation. Would a month with him work it out of her system?

She'd never experienced anything quite like this before. Was it something that *could* be worked out or was it something that would grow . . . ? How was she going to feel at the end of the month?

Panicked, her eyes flew open and she jammed in the remaining rose with an angry gesture. What was the matter with her? She wasn't obligated to live with him for a month in spite of what he claimed. She was sharp, clever, and infinitely more skilled at handling people than Lang Sterling was. She could handle him. Damn it! She would have his name on that contract, and her freedom, too!

"Miss me this morning?" he drawled, turning to watch her as she came back into the living room with the roses.

"Did you slip out early to try and teach me a lesson for having done it to you yesterday morning?" she asked lightly, not quite meeting his eyes as she set down the flowers.

"Not really." He grinned. "To tell you the truth, I thought it might be a wise idea to be out of the way when you awoke and put that manipulating little mind of yours to work on the problem at hand. Come to any brilliant conclusions?"

"You don't seem very worried by the possibility!"

"I'm not. I'm a simple man with a simple plan. Simple plans are the hardest to foul up," he explained kindly. "You'll be moving in with me or"—he glanced around the room in open speculation—"I'll be moving in with you quite soon."

Behind the frames of her glasses, Kali arched a quelling brow. "*How* soon?"

"Depends on how quickly you want to conclude the patent deal for IAI," he retorted, taking another sip of Scotch. "I'm not signing anything, though, until you and I have wrapped up our own private arrangement."

"And if I refuse?" she asked carefully.

"Then I'll keep carrying you off to bed until you agree,"

142

he returned, unperturbed. "Come on, honey, let's go. I'm starving!"

The restaurant Lang had chosen in the charmingly restored section of Seattle called Pioneer Square was romantic, eclectic, and very intimate. Exactly the sort of place one of his ancestors might have selected for an assignation with a mistress, Kali decided wryly as she opened her menu.

"Why the mysterious little smile?" he demanded softly as he glanced up from studying the wine list.

"Do mysterious little feminine smiles bother simple men with simple plans?" she taunted lightly.

"Smiles like that one have been bothering every man since the world began! Why do you think we're still going around asking the old question of what do women want?"

"I can tell you what I want," she returned briskly. "Your signature on a contract with IAI."

He winced. "Ask a silly question."

"You said yesterday you were bringing me here to talk business tonight."

"There are other things in life besides business, Kali. Someday I'm going to succeed in getting that through your head and when I do I will feel I've made a major breakthrough in the field of robotics!"

The humor in her faded. "I'm not a robot, Lang. I'm beginning to resent comments like that last one!"

"That's a good sign," he assured her as the waiter approached. "Nalg would never in a million years be capable of resentment at being labeled a robot!"

Kali's polite expression slipped but there was nothing more she could say as the waiter prepared to take their orders. The formally attired, aloof-looking individual hovered over her attentively, and she obediently began to list her first course, only to have Lang interrupt as soon as she'd named the beet and cucumber salad.

"No, no," he interposed with such authority that the waiter instantly paid attention. "We'll share one of the fish and pistachio terrines for a first course, I think." He mused a second longer. "And then the hearts of artichoke salad. After that I think the Coquilles Saint-Jacques for the lady . . . you do like scallops, don't you, darling?"

Kali, having all she could do to contain her irritation, managed an indignant nod. She would not make a scene in front of the waiter. She hated public scenes!

"I'll have the sea bass with fennel and we'll split the minted vegetables. And a bottle of the '77 Chardonnay, please."

Kali threw her escort a stony glance as the waiter hurried off. She'd never had a man presume to order for her in her entire life.

"Don't look at me like that," he protested. "You're going to love what I selected." The near-green eyes gleamed with muted amusement and some of the wariness she had seen before in him.

"What makes you think you know what I want?"

"I know what's best for you," he murmured soothingly. "Trust me."

Kali lifted helpless eyes toward heaven in a beseeching glance, but she kept her temper. Business first. If she was going to manipulate this evening successfully, she was going to have to use her energy only on the important battles.

He eyed her determined expression and threw up a hand in mock surrender. "Okay, okay. Let's get the business part of this affair out of the way."

Kali's gaze narrowed behind the lenses of her glasses at the word "affair." He had not used it accidentally, she was certain. But she chose not to call attention to it.

"Lang, let me spell out exactly what IAI can offer . . ."

He leaned forward, propping his chin on the heel of his hand as he braced his elbow on the white tablecloth. The thick russet lashes lowered invitingly and he smiled politely. He was indulging her and Kali could have kicked him for it. Nevertheless she launched into her list of benefits and advantages, elaborating on each one. By the time she had finished, the fish terrine had arrived.

"So you see," she concluded bravely, aware that his attention was wandering to the food, "not only can IAI provide you with the cash you want, we'll also make available the accounting services which will help you protect and shelter that cash. Furthermore, you'll receive a regular stipend while you're using our lab facilities . . ."

"No."

Kali, caught in full flight, faltered. "I beg your pardon?" She blinked owlishly, watching as he used a small knife to spread the appetizer on a cracker.

"I won't be needing the lab facilities so you can keep your stipend," he explained easily, handing her the cracker he'd prepared.

Kali accepted it automatically, staring at him. "Surely IAI can provide far more sophisticated experimental equipment that you have already! Every inventor needs the best possible lab facilities!"

"Not if he's getting out of the robot-inventing business!"

"What!" Now she really was floundering. "I don't understand, Lang. Don't you want to continue your work in robotics?"

He set down his knife and faced her squarely. "Nalg is my last venture into robotics, Kali."

She saw the absolute determination in him and shook her head uncomprehendingly. "But why, Lang? It's your life. It's what you do best . . ."

"Why?" he repeated slowly, all hint of indulgence gone from his expression as he held her concerned gaze in a green net. He leaned forward with sudden intensity. "I'll tell you why, Kali. Because, with only a few minor adjustments in his programming, I could put a gun in Nalg's claw and send him rolling down the sidewalk with instructions to shoot anything that moved. He'd do it without a second's hesitation."

"My God!" Kali stared at the man across from her. "What are you saying, Lang?"

"That the field of robotics has gone far enough. I'm not making any more contributions to it. Period." He sat back and spread another cracker with the fish and pistachio mixture.

The tense seconds ticked past while Kali tried to absorb what he was saying.

"He . . . it's only a machine, Lang . . ."

"A *programmable* machine. He could be programmed to kill."

"Or to assist a doctor in a hospital!" she tossed back immediately.

Lang nodded. "Yes. There's that side of the picture, I agree. But given the nature of the human race, I'm willing to bet that for every healing machine there will probably be a killing machine. I want no further part of the business."

Kali hesitated, aware of his conviction and uncertain how to deal with it. She felt torn. On the one hand, she had an obligation to try and talk him into coming to work for IAI. On the other, she felt a powerful and totally unfamiliar wish to urge him to do as his inner convictions demanded. It struck her that this was the first time in her entire career that she had faced such a situation. Always before her priorities had been crystal clear. Whatever was good for the company was good for her career . . .

"You know that the technology in the field is moving very fast, Lang . . ." she began almost gently.

146

"And if I don't pursue it someone else will? I know that. I'm not foolish enough to think I can stop progress in its tracks. I'm just not going to contribute to it anymore." The edge of his mouth lifted mockingly but the bronze-green eyes were steady and watchful.

"What . . . what will you do?"

"For a new career?" He hesitated a split second and Kali had the impression he was almost uncertain about telling her the next part. Then he appeared to reach a decision. "I'm going to try my hand at writing."

"Writing what?"

"Science fiction."

"Science fiction!" she repeated, thunderstruck. "I thought you'd seen the future already and weren't too thrilled about it! Why science fiction, for heaven's sake? Why not adventure novels of the past or something?"

"Because it's the future which needs romanticizing," he explained simply. "The past has already been romanticized."

Kali considered that, her food forgotten. "I hadn't thought about it quite that way," she whispered slowly. She sat very quietly for a moment, considering the statement. "Perhaps you're right. Perhaps it's the literature of romance and adventure and deeds of derring-do set in the future which will help us handle a world full of cold machines."

"It's a way of remembering our humanity, remembering that our passions are more important than the programmed responses of our machines. What would be the point of living in a world without romance? It's our tales and songs and legends which keep romance alive and science fiction is comprised of the sagas and legends of the future. The way the world is going, we need those tales before we actually arrive in the future."

"Because we can use them to shape that future?" Kali concluded.

Lang met her eyes across the table and smiled. She could have sworn there was a shade of relief in that smile, a fading of some of the wariness. For a moment there was complete and total understanding between them.

Such moments were dangerous, Kali realized as the delicate structure of it was shattered by the arrival of the waiter. Such moments could change one's life.

But she didn't want her life changed, she thought protestingly to herself throughout the remainder of dinner. She had her priorities straight and she certainly didn't need an unabashed romantic from the past who was intent on applying his principles to the future interfering with her carefully programmed world.

Programmed! Good Lord! What had made her use that word!

Somehow the conversation never returned to the business topic Kali had been so intent on discussing. She made a few halfhearted attempts to get back to the matter of the contract for the patents, but the ease with which she let herself be led off into unrelated subjects convinced her that, deep down, she really didn't want to talk business with this man tonight. The very word was beginning to make her rather nervous, in fact.

And that wasn't the only thing which was making her nervous that evening, she thought as Lang eventually bundled her gently into a taxi and took her home. The use of the taxi reminded her of the expensive sports car he had on order. Time was running out for both of them. Lang was going to need money soon and she was going to have to find a way of dealing with his incredible demands for finalizing the deal with IAI. Most certainly she was not going to simply move in with him! But she put even that problem out of her mind as she faced the decision of

148

whether or not to ask him up to her apartment for a nightcap.

It had, somewhat to her shock, turned into an intriguing, warm, and magical evening. But there could be only one ending to it if she allowed him upstairs. Once Lang took her into his arms, she would be lost until morning. From somewhere Kali found the courage to face that realization.

In a totally un-Kali-like manner, she managed to dither over the matter until it was abruptly too late to take a stand. She found herself being escorted out of the cab and into the condominium lobby before she could find the words to end the evening.

By the time the elevator arrived it was too late. Kali knew a strange relaxation as she realized she wouldn't be able to halt the inevitable conclusion now.

At her door Lang took her key and ushered her inside. As if by unspoken agreement, Kali crossed the floor to sink languidly down onto the yellow sofa. She watched through lowered lids as Lang paced calmly over to the liquor cabinet, found the expensive Armagnac, and poured it into two snifters.

Without a word he carried them back to the couch, sitting close to her and handing her one of the crystal glasses.

"Thank you for the lovely evening, Kali." He smiled, breaking the silence which had begun in the taxi.

"We . . . we didn't get much business accomplished," she whispered throatily, feeling pleasantly hypnotized by the bonds of his gaze. She was glad she didn't have to think anymore this evening. She wanted only to give herself up to the night and Lang's arms . . .

"I think we accomplished something much more important," he returned huskily.

Once again the strange communion flowed between

149

them and Kali felt the now-welcome shivers of anticipation.

They finished the Armagnac in a companionable silence interspersed with soft, meaningless talk, meaningless, at any rate, to an outsider. When Lang finally set down his snifter and got slowly to his feet, Kali did the same, her eyes gentle and warming with the soon-to-be-aroused passion.

"Good night, sweetheart," he growled, catching her throat with one hand and holding her still for his kiss. Then he lifted his head, staring down at her expectant face with a brooding passion for a moment longer before turning on his heel and heading for the door.

Kali watched in disbelief as the door shut behind him.

It was the first of several evenings which ended in exactly the same, unsatisfying fashion for Kali. The pattern of each was similar: a charming, intimate dinner, conversation which lingered over the Armagnac, and Lang's final good night kiss.

She told herself he was playing some kind of game with her emotions, but when she admitted that possibility it meant admitting he had the power to do so. A devastating admission.

She told herself he was using sex or lack thereof as a weapon. But to admit that meant he had a physical dominance over her that no other man had possessed. Before she'd met Lang Sterling, Kali would never have believed she could feel such a stomach-twisting level of desire. That admission was not any less unsettling than the first.

She told herself she would put a stop to the evenings out unless she could get Lang to finish his business with IAI. But she couldn't bring herself to lay down the ultimatum. Kali had never had much difficulty taking a position and enforcing it before in her life. Positive action which moved the game forward was the only route she knew. It was infinitely disturbing to have to admit Lang had the power to short-circuit her normal way of doing business.

But the most disturbing, unnerving, unsettling thing of all was the way she ended each evening alone, staring silently out into the darkness and trying to come to grips with the realization that Lang Sterling's greatest power was his unexpected ability to make her question her single-minded devotion to her career at IAI.

Because after each evening out with Lang she cared more about his future than she cared about IAI's.

And that admission was enough to make any successful vice-president quake in her hundred-dollar leather business pumps.

She was literally terrified, she realized at the end of the week as she stood before the darkened window. There was only one word for the emotion which might be strong enough to account for her chaotic reactions to Lang Sterling.

And the prospect of being in love with this man from another era didn't please Kali one bit.

She shied instinctively from the word but she couldn't dodge the reality of the mess in which she found herself. For there was an expression which had been coined long ago in the business world to describe this kind of situation.

CHAPTER NINE

"It's called a conflict of interest, Max, and there's only one acceptable way of managing it. I have to remove myself from the negotiations between Lang Sterling and IAI."

Kali faced the assessing look in her boss's cool eyes with a determined matter-of-factness she was far from feeling. But her decision had been reached during the long hours of the previous night when she had lain awake alone in her bed and realized the precariously balanced scale on which she had been standing had finally tipped. When Lang had taken her in his arms after dinner last night she had finally acknowledged that the time had come to stop using euphemisms for the emotions she was feeling. She was in love.

There was no logic behind the vibrant, incredibly disturbing sensation as far as she could determine but that only seemed to make it all the more powerful. Logic could be dealt with in her world. Magic was something else again.

Max Spencer eyed his junior vice-president keenly and once again Kali found herself thinking that in the several

152

months she had worked directly for him there was still a lot she didn't know about Maxwell Spencer. She had been so careful to keep a strict, formal distance between them and he had not made any efforts to overcome that space. They were colleagues but not really friends in anything other than the most formal associations of the word. Now Max deliberately stepped over the carefully drawn, invisible boundaries.

"Are you trying to tell me you're involved with Lang Sterling?"

Kali kept her composure with an effort. "You don't believe in being delicate about business, do you, Max?" she noted whimsically.

"Not with this kind of potential at stake," he agreed dryly. "Kali, I don't, in all honesty, see the problem, even if you are having an affair with the man. The deal we're offering Sterling is a good one, an excellent one from his point of view and our own. In this case the interests of both parties would seem to, er, coincide. Where's the conflict?"

"Max!" Kali's self-control was swamped in the blush that rushed into her face. "I can't go on conducting business as usual with a man I'm . . . I'm . . ." She broke off, chagrined.

Her boss's mouth crooked. "Kali, you amaze me. I thought you could conduct business with just about anyone under just about any circumstances. You were well trained."

"I know," she whispered dryly. "I know. Max, I'm sorry to let you down like this. I'll understand if you want my resignation . . ."

He ignored that with grand indifference just as if he hadn't a notion of what it had cost her to make the offer. Or, thought Kali in a sudden flash of intuition, perhaps he ignored it so completely precisely because he had realized

153

how much it had cost! Was it possible he was subtly trying to let her know how ridiculous he considered her offer? In spite of the trying circumstances, she felt herself warming slightly. Walking into the boss's office and letting him know you could no longer carry out an assignment because you'd fallen in love with the man you were supposed to be doing business with was hardly the ideal way to improve communications between two professional executives! But he wasn't taking the news at all as she had expected . . . He seemed almost *understanding*.

"Have you informed Sterling yet of your decision?" Max asked, tapping a gold pen absently on his black glass desk.

"No. I'm going to call him as soon as I leave here. I planned on telling him he would be dealing with Mike from here on if that's all right with you?" she said tentatively.

"You think Jarvis can handle things?"

Kali nodded. "I think Lang is ready to sell and he's reasonably satisfied with IAI's offer. What he's listened to of it, that is," she added ruefully. "By the way, he is definitely not going to be part of any deal with any firm. He wants out of the robot business!"

Max frowned. "You're sure of that?"

"No question." Kali shook her head with great certainty. "And you don't have to worry about him selling the patents to one firm and going to work for another, either."

"What's he going to do? The man's brilliant in his field!" Max looked almost pained at the apparent waste of talent.

"He's going to try his hand at writing science fiction," Kali admitted wryly.

Max stared at her and then he gave a chuckle of deep laughter. "You're kidding!"

154

"Nope. And I have a hunch it's going to be the kind of sci-fi in which the robots don't win."

Spencer cocked a graying, shaggy brow. "Don't tell me, an engineer-inventor with a social conscience?" But Max wasn't sneering, Kali realized. He sounded almost distantly admiring.

From out of nowhere Kali found herself remembering the small fact that IAI had never become involved with defense contracts. That had bothered Davis Wakefield and from time to time he had made forceful presentations to his superiors on the subject of going after some of the lucrative weapons research money.

Max had always claimed he steered IAI clear of government business because of the roller-coaster nature of federal funds. Now Kali wondered if there weren't other reasons for the fact that IAI routinely ignored bidding opportunities on military development projects. Could it be that Maxwell Spencer had some very private thoughts on the morality of applying the technology of robotics to military use? If so, that suited her just fine. She had made no effort to follow in Davis's footsteps in that one particular area. There had been no forceful presentations from her on going after weapons contracts!

"I don't know that I'd say Lang is afflicted with a 'social conscience.' That always implies strident protest in the streets, doesn't it? But I think you could say the man has a very *human* approach to life. Past, present, and future! He seems to move quite blithely back and forth among all three. But there are times when I think . . ." She bit her tongue, shocked to hear herself discussing such things with Maxwell Spencer!

"When you think what, Kali?" he asked gently.

"When I think he probably should have been born a couple of hundred years ago. Look, Max, I'm very sorry about this whole mess. I know I've gotten myself into an

155

untenable situation and there is absolutely no excuse . . ."

"There's always the excuse of being human," he murmured.

She slanted him a curious glance, uncertain of his meaning, and then pressed gamely on. "There shouldn't be any problem letting Mike handle things from here on. The experience will be good for him."

"I respect your judgment of the situation, Kali. If you're sure this is the way you want to handle matters . . ."

"It is," she declared firmly, grateful for his support and understanding. She had expected neither. "And, again, I'm very sorry . . ."

"Conflict-of-interest situations can happen to anyone doing business on this kind of level," he returned calmly. "Believe me, there are far more appalling ways of developing a conflict of interest than by falling in love! At least I don't have to worry about you taking bribes or letting yourself be pirated away by a rival firm, taking the patents with you!"

She stared at him. "How . . . how did you know?"

Spencer smiled grimly. "That Wakefield was in town and might try to buy you and Sterling both? I'm not president of the company for nothing, Kali. Once I found out Hadley was in on the chase, the rest were obvious conclusions. So he did try?"

"It wasn't a very tempting offer, Max." She grinned suddenly. "After all, it would have meant moving to California. What kind of a fool would do that?"

He laughed. "I'm vastly reassured. Okay, let's concentrate on bringing Mike up to speed on the situation. Have my secretary arrange a meeting for all of us this afternoon, will you?" Max was abruptly all business again and Kali quickly assumed her proper role.

But she still had her job and, apparently, her boss's respect when she left his office a few moments later. Since she had fully expected to leave without at least one of the two, she felt a surging sense of relief. If that had been Davis Wakefield sitting in the IAI president's chair, she would no longer have either.

Funny, she'd never realized there was that much difference between Davis and Max. Perhaps she'd been taught to view Max through Davis's eyes and Davis saw everyone as either a manipulator or one of the manipulated. He'd had a certain respect for Max Spencer and therefore saw the older man as a manipulator. Kali wondered how much of her own view of Spencer had been established by Davis's attitude. It wasn't until today that she'd begun to realize there was a human side to Maxwell Spencer.

"Joanna," she said in a steady voice as she came through the office door, "would you please see if you can track down Lang Sterling for me?"

"Right away, Kali."

I ought to have foreseen this mess days ago, Kali thought morosely as she took the chair behind her desk. But how could she have realized the effect Lang would have on her? How could she have guessed that any man could have the power to put her in such a position?

There was no arguing with facts, however, and if there was one thing Kali knew she was good at, it was dealing with hard, cold facts.

She was in love.

That much was a fact. The corollary to it was that Lang wanted her. Passionately. Romantically. And he had the power to make her feel the same toward him. She didn't know if his passion would turn to love but she knew she needed desperately to find out if it could.

To do that she needed to be free of the conflict of interest in which she found herself.

For how could she go to him as part of a business deal? Lang Sterling needed a woman who could reciprocate his romantic passion fully. A woman whom he knew beyond any shadow of a doubt had come to him because she wanted him and for no other reason. Especially not business reasons!

"Kali, I've got Sterling on the line." Joanna's voice through the intercom held a faintly curious note.

"Thanks, Joanna." Kali picked up her receiver, grimacing slightly as she realized her hand wasn't quite steady. Damn it! If ever there was a time to be calm, cool, and totally collected, this was it!

"Hello, sweetheart, what's up?" Lang's deep, gritty voice came through the line with a ruffling effect on Kali's nerves. For an instant she remembered how he had looked last night just before he'd kissed her farewell at her door. The bronze-green eyes had shimmered with the banked fires of desire and there had been a hint of trembling in the excitingly rough palm which had cupped her face.

With that image in her mind, Kali knew that what she was about to do was right. She had to be free to explore what lay beneath Lang's passion. She had to take the risk.

She drew a long, steadying breath. "Lang, I'm calling you to tell you that I've taken myself out of the negotiations between you and Interactive Automation . . ."

She got no further. The telephone seemed to explode in her hand.

"You've done *what!*" The gritty voice was suddenly a panther's roar.

"You heard me, Lang. It was the only way . . ."

"The hell it was! What game do you think you're playing with me now, Kali Havelock?" Kali was forced to hold the phone a couple of inches away from her ear. "I never had you pegged as a coward!"

"I'm not playing games!" In spite of her resolve, Kali

158

had the awful impression she was close to shouting herself. "Because of you I'm in a . . . a *conflict-of-interest* situation, don't you understand? I have no choice but to take myself out of the business dealings going on between you and my company. You'll be dealing with my assistant, Mike Jarvis. I'm sure you'll find him very efficient and he will have full power to represent the firm . . ."

"I'm sure he's efficient as hell! You probably trained him! But that doesn't matter one bit, Madame Robot, you're the only representative of IAI I'm dealing with. I refuse to start all over with someone else at this point!"

"How can you say that? You've hardly even started dealing with me! Every time I bring up business you change the subject. In any event, Mike will be thoroughly briefed on what IAI can offer. He'll know exactly where we left off . . ."

"You'd tell him something that personal?" Lang taunted furiously.

"You know what I mean!"

"Damn right I know what you mean," he shot back. "Lost your nerve, didn't you? You think you can ease out of my life as easily as you manipulated yourself into it!"

"You're wrong there!" Kali gritted, infuriated now. "It was a whole lot easier getting into your life. All I had to do was find out you were dating Gwen Mather and then arrange to get her invited to Amanda Bryant's reception. The rest was a fait accompli! A snap compared to what I'm trying to do at the moment!" *Nice going,* Kali told herself wretchedly as she listened to her own words. *You never used to have this problem of knowing when to keep your mouth shut!*

"After going to all that trouble you better believe I'm making sure you stay until the end," he rasped. "Conflict of interest, am I? Well, you're about to find out how much interesting conflict I can generate when the provocation is sufficient, woman! We had a bargain, you and I . . ."

"I won't be part of any bargain!"

"You already are! There's no conflict of interest here that I can see! Your company wants my patents and I'm willing to sell them!"

"For a price!" she reminded him meaningfully.

"If you think you can escape what we have together by refusing to be part of the price IAI pays for those damn patents, you're a whole lot less intelligent than the average industrial robot!"

"I'm not looking for a way to escape you or what—what we might have, Lang Sterling," Kali nearly yelled into the receiver. Never had she had so much trouble controlling her reactions! *I'm looking for a way to come to you with no strings attached!*"

Immediately she wished she'd found another way of phrasing that. She hadn't meant to go quite that far initially. But she did a lot of things around Lang that she didn't intend, Kali reflected bleakly.

The astounded silence on the other end of the line was truly deafening.

"No strings?" Lang finally repeated cautiously. "Kali, are you saying you're removing yourself from the deal so that you can come to me of your own accord? You don't want me thinking you're only doing it to secure the patents?"

She wished he wouldn't be quite so blunt about such delicate matters. "I would like our . . . our relationship or whatever it is to develop independently of outside business influences," Kali said very stiffly, grateful he couldn't see the red stain on her cheeks.

"Conflict of interest," he interrupted in tones of awe. "So that's what this is all about."

"Lang, I'm trying to explain . . ."

160

"Conflict of interest," he repeated again, sounding as if he were tasting the word and finding it nectar. "Conflict of interest. Damn if that isn't the most romantic thing anyone has ever said to me!"

"Lang . . . !"

There was a click as he hung up the phone in her ear.

Kali was left staring at the silent instrument in her hand. What in the world was going on now? With a horrible sensation that everything was getting completely out of hand, Kali removed her glasses and massaged the bridge of her nose in a gesture of anxiety.

She wasn't left to ponder her chaotic future long. Ten minutes after Lang had hung up on her, Max's secretary was summoning her to the president's office.

"What's going on, Kali?" Spencer demanded without preamble as she opened his inner door with a polite look of professional inquiry. "I just had a call from Sterling."

"What did he want?" she breathed, startled.

"To finalize the fate of his patents was the way he put it. After all the stalling for the past week it seems he's suddenly decided to end the business one way or another. He sounded," Max went on, steepling his fingers in front of him as he watched Kali's expression, "as if he were in somewhat of a hurry."

Kali sat down shakily. "Oh, my God!"

"That's not quite the competent, alert, thoroughly-in-charge response I expect from my executive staff in moments of crisis."

Kali winced. "Sorry. The only other descriptive phrases I can think of at the moment aren't really suited to the executive suite either. More like the docks."

"Don't kid yourself," he retorted with the smallest hint of humor. "The executive suite has been known to sound like a dockyard in its time. Well, let's get things under control," he went on briskly.

"Right," she nodded, striving to do as bid. "He sounded as if he finally meant business?"

"He did."

"Then I'd better dig up Mike and go over matters with him in a hurry."

"There isn't time," Max drawled quietly. "Sterling is going to meet us shortly at a nearby restaurant. If he can get hold of Davis Wakefield, that is."

"Davis!"

"It would appear Lang has decided to get his bidding war on after all. With a vengeance."

Kali's mouth went dry. What had she precipitated? "I see. Are you going to handle the negotiations, then, instead of Mike?"

"Sterling says he'll only deal with you on the IAI side. Claims the indulgence due an eccentric inventor," Max told her dryly.

"Oh, no!"

"Your second brilliant statement since entering the room."

"Sir, I've explained the situation to him," Kali breathed earnestly. "I told him he'd be dealing with Mike."

"Which he apparently has no desire to do."

She closed her eyes, stifling a low groan. "I know I haven't handled this at all well . . ."

"But you will shortly have an opportunity to redeem yourself, won't you?" Max's expression softened. "Don't look so stricken, Kali. You can handle it and you know it. This will be all business. You did the right thing, the ethical thing, when you tried to remove yourself from the situation. But, as Lang implied, there's no accounting for the eccentricities of a genius roboticist. He refuses to negotiate with any other representative of the firm and that's that. I have complete trust in your abilities to perform the job."

"Even against Davis Wakefield?" she murmured carefully. Now that Lang knew he could have her without turning over the patents everyone had entered a whole new ball game. Lang wouldn't have tried to restart the bidding war unless he were seriously interested in hearing the competition's offer again.

"Even against Davis Wakefield. Come on, Kali. We have a luncheon appointment." Max Spencer rose purposefully and Kali, taking a grip on herself, did the same.

She wasn't at all prepared for the shock which awaited her as she walked into the handsome, subdued atmosphere of the restaurant Lang had chosen. It wasn't the sight of him sharing a drink at the bar with Davis Wakefield which provided the shock; it was Lang himself.

He looked, she realized in wonder, thoroughly and arrogantly at home among the crowd of executives patronizing the establishment. She watched him leaning casually against the polished bar, sipping Scotch, and silently shook her head at the understated, eminently successful look of the charcoal-gray suit, crisp white shirt, and quietly striped tie that would have done justice to any chairman of the board.

He was wearing the attire of the present, but he dominated the room because he wore the style and arrogance of the past as if it were second nature. Did he really move through time warps, Kali asked herself bemusedly as she walked forward beside Max, or was it simply that some men would always seem intriguingly at odds with their surroundings because they cut their own paths through those surroundings? Their bold, very human masculinity made them nonconformists automatically.

Lang was talking with Davis who, if he'd been a cat, Kali decided, would have been purring loudly. Instinctively she tensed. She didn't need anyone to tell her that Davis

Wakefield was supremely confident of his abilities. He was still the master and she only the apprentice.

Both men glanced up, still smiling politely from a comment one of them had made, as Kali and Max came forward. Across the room Lang's eyes met Kali's and there was a flare of deepest green in the look of naked possessiveness which skimmed her neat little black suit, sleekly knotted hair, and businesslike glasses.

She felt her body reacting to the look but before she could summon so much as a quelling frown, Lang had blanked the expression, replacing it with one of cool, magnificently aloof formality. He extended his hand to shake Max's.

"I'm Lang Sterling," he said easily. "I understand you want to buy some patents from me."

"Very much," Max returned urbanely, turning to Davis. "Wakefield. Good to see you again. I hear you're doing very well for yourself down in California."

"Even better after I buy Sterling's patents out from under you." Davis chuckled.

"You'll have to get past Kali in order to do that." Max smiled.

"She's going to handle the negotiations for you?" Davis flicked an amused glance at his former assistant.

Kali stood her ground as the eyes of all three men turned in her direction. She could read nothing at all now in Lang's gaze. Nothing, that was, except business. She returned the cool, polite smiles with one of her best as Max answered Davis's question.

"Yes, she will."

"Should be interesting," Davis observed, sipping his martini reflectively. "Sterling assures me this is an honest little bidding war he's initiated, though. No, uh, hidden inducements . . ." He slanted another meaningful glance at Kali.

"None," Lang said in a low, cold tone before Kali could answer. "The patents go to the bidder who can offer me the most satisfactory deal. And, as I've explained, I, personally, don't go with the patents."

"This isn't exactly a normal method of competition," Max noted calmly.

"I try not to be too heavily influenced by routine approaches to situations," Lang drawled politely. "Shall we get started? I've reserved a table."

Kali watched him carefully out of the corner of her eye as the four of them walked to a nearby table. Under the polite, superficial conversation which ensued while the luncheon orders were taken, she put every intuitive nerve she possessed on the alert.

One overwhelming message came through. This really was all business. Lang had been telling the truth. He wasn't going to hand over the valuable patents because of her, not any longer. He knew she would be coming to him regardless of the outcome of today's bidding. The possession in his first glance had told her part of the story. The maverick, highly unorthodox, but thoroughly professional way he was doing business today told her the rest.

A part of her relaxed even as another part came fully aware. She would need all of her faculties if she were to stand a chance of holding her own against Davis Wakefield. He clearly saw no threat in her at all now.

Coolly, with the poker-faced politeness of two sophisticated gamblers, each put forth the offers of their respective companies. Lang listened attentively, while dining on the fresh salmon he had ordered. Whenever he queried an offer, either Davis or Kali bettered it or threw in a fringe benefit.

But there were limits to what IAI could afford and Max and Kali had gone over them thoroughly in the past. No

165

one knew for certain how far Hadley Industrial Systems would go to obtain the patents.

It soon became obvious, however, that the answer to that question was, very high. Ultimately, the best cash offer was Hadley's.

"Don't forget that IAI will be happy to provide access to professionals who can help you shelter the kind of money involved here so that you don't lose it all to the IRS," Kali tried, knowing it wasn't a strong enough inducement. "We will also be willing to pay for the services of an attorney for you who can oversee the drawing up of the contracts . . ."

"Hadley will throw in any accounting or legal services you may require," Davis interjected smoothly. "And we'll handle all the business transactions up here in Washington if you like so that there will be no need for a trip down to California. If you choose to make the trip, we'll pick up the expenses, naturally."

Inwardly, Kali groaned. She was going to lose those patents to Hadley. She knew it. Davis was willing to top anything she was in a position to offer. Hadley Industrial must want those new sensors very, very badly. She wondered if Davis had a specific reason other than merely getting a jump on the industrial robot market. Desperately she racked her brain, trying to remember what she had read recently of important contracts being let by various companies and the government. Normally, she made it a point to keep thoroughly abreast of such matters.

"I think that's about it, then." Lang nodded as he flicked a last, inquiring glance at Kali before turning to Davis.

Kali shot a questioning look at her boss, who almost imperceptibly shook his head. IAI would go no further in the bidding.

"This is a straightforward business deal," Lang was

166

saying calmly. "I really don't need any more time to consider the matter and I think I've heard your best offers. So . . ." He looked at Davis.

Inspiration struck Kali. It might not be much of a chance, but what did she have to lose now? Hastily she put together everything she knew about IAI, Hadley Industrial, and the various personalities involved and threw in her knowledge of recent news in the field.

"I wonder," she murmured quietly, just as Lang opened his mouth to accept Davis's offer, "if you would consider an alternative to an outright sale of those patents."

Instantly she was the sole focus of attention. Kali felt Max's questioning eyes but didn't turn to look at him. She had her hands full.

"What are you talking about?" Lang asked softly.

"I'm talking about licensing IAI to produce robots utilizing your patents. It's true, there wouldn't be nearly as much money up front as there would be in an outright sale, but there would be a steady income from the license fees IAI would pay over the years . . ."

"Why should he do that?" Davis snapped, annoyed. He had almost had the rabbit in his snare and he knew it. "Sterling has made it clear he wants to take the money in one large chunk and IAI can't match what Hadley is prepared to offer. If you are interested in merely licensing, rather than selling the patents, Sterling, we can negotiate, but I don't see what advantage that would have for you . . ."

"It would have the advantage," Kali pointed out coolly, "of allowing him to put restrictions on how the patents were applied."

There was a heavy silence around the table. But the sudden gleam in Max's quiet gaze told Kali he was the first to realize the full implications. He said nothing, however, leaving everything to her.

167

"What are you saying, Kali?" Lang asked deliberately.

"I'm saying that IAI would be happy to guarantee in writing that any robots or related equipment made under your patent license would be strictly for industrial use. IAI does not take military contracts from the government."

"What the hell difference does that make?" Davis rapped.

"IAI would be willing to have such an agreement written into the licensing arrangement?" Lang persisted with a sudden intentness as he met Kali's eyes levelly.

"Yes." She nodded, not even bothering to glance at Max for confirmation. She was sure of herself on these grounds. "The patents would not be applied to any military or weapons-related use."

Lang turned once more to Davis. "Would Hadley be willing to sign such a clause if I were to elect to license the patents instead of sell them?"

"Impossible! Hadley is deeply involved in federal contracts! We'd be cutting our own throats if we were to sign such a clause. Look, Sterling, what difference does it make to you how the patents are ultimately utilized? Money is money!"

"And business is business," Lang returned, sitting back in his chair and smiling blandly at Kali and Max. "I said in the beginning I would hand the patents over to whoever gave me the most satisfactory deal. If IAI is willing to sign a no-weapons-use clause, I'm happy to license the firm to produce robots based on my sensor patents."

"IAI will be very pleased to sign such a contract," Max said, speaking for the first time since the negotiations had begun.

"This is ridiculous!" Davis swore as he stood up, and tossed his napkin down on the table. "IAI never did have any common sense about dealing with the government on

168

military contracts! And you're a fool to throw away the kind of money my firm can offer, Sterling! The license fees won't match what you could have had up front from Hadley!"

"I realize that," Lang replied quietly. "What you apparently fail to realize is that there are other things of importance in the world besides money."

"You're all fools!" Davis hissed angrily. "Thank God I got out of IAI when I did! It would have made me sick to work with this kind of blindness to the realities of business!"

He turned and strode off through the crowded dining room, never looking back.

Kali, Max, and Lang stared after him for a long moment, each thinking his or her own thoughts.

Then, slowly, they turned back to each other.

"You're satisfied with the deal?" Max asked easily, just as if he hadn't witnessed a major scene from a former vice-president.

"I'm satisfied," Lang confirmed, confronting the older man. There was a silent second of man-to-man understanding between them which made Kali smile to herself —two men who would have been mortally offended if someone had accused either of them of displaying any kind of unrealistic social conscience.

Then Lang's warming glance swung back to Kali. "You sent the right person to handle the job, Max."

Max smiled cryptically, tossing a last glance at the door through which Davis Wakefield had disappeared.

"When it comes to dealing with robots like Davis Wakefield," he announced on a soft chuckle, "I'll put my money on a human being every time. Congratulations, Kali. Now," he added, getting to his feet, "if you'll excuse me, I think I'll be getting back to the office. No, that's all right," he told Kali lightly as she obediently made to follow. "I think it would be a good idea if you stayed here and worked out the finer points of the contract with Mr. Sterling. I'm sure he's anxious to tie up all the loose ends. Oh, don't worry about the check, either of you," he added dryly, reaching for it. "IAI can afford to pick it up."

He disappeared, leaving Kali sitting across the table from the man to whom she had silently given her heart. All the cool, sophisticated business expression was gone from Lang's bronze-green gaze. Twin devils of desire and satisfied possession looked out of the near-green depths now. Kali struggled valiantly for something light and witty to ease the tension of the moment. Nothing very brilliant came to mind.

"You amaze me," she managed to whisper. "You would have made an excellent businessman."

"And you," he returned, reaching for her hand and pulling her lightly to her feet as he rose, "make a lousy robot. Come home with me, sweetheart, I have something very important to discuss with you. Something regarding a conflict of interest."

170

CHAPTER TEN

"Will you mind not getting fabulously rich off those patents?" Kali asked tentatively as Lang stuffed her into a cab and gave directions to his home on Capitol Hill.

"No." He sat back against the upholstery, putting an arm around her shoulders and pulling her close to his side. He had the air of a man who is very pleased with himself.

"The nice thing about a licensing arrangement is that there is a steady sum of money coming in on a regular basis," she went on determinedly. "And we can arrange a large enough sum in the beginning so that you can pay off all your bills . . ."

"Yes," he agreed, smiling down into her anxious face.

"You're not listening to me, are you?"

"No."

She sighed suspiciously. "What are you thinking about, Lang?"

"I'll tell you when we get home."

He said nothing else the rest of the way, tipped the taxi driver outrageously when they arrived, and led her up to the front door with an eager determination.

"Where's Nalg?" Kali exclaimed in surprise as they let themselves into the quiet hall.

"I dismantled him," Lang told her with a dismissing shrug as he shut the door behind them and reached for her.

"You what!"

"Dismantled him. It was getting too tempting to anthropomorphize him, you know, treat him-it as if it were part human. Don't look at me like that! It was hardly a case of murder!"

"I had plans for that robot," Kali retorted spiritedly. "He-it had such a way with dishes and he, uh, it kept such a clean house. Did Nalg do windows, too?"

"Under protest." Lang chuckled, wrapping his strong hands around her neck and dragging her close. "That was something else which had begun to worry me. Machines aren't supposed to protest!"

"You're teasing me!"

"Maybe," he drawled softly, bending slightly to feather the tip of her ear with his lips. "And maybe not. It doesn't matter. I want to talk about conflicts of interest at the moment, not robots."

Kali trembled slightly as she sensed the waiting warmth in him. "What . . . what about conflicts of interest, Lang?"

He groaned huskily. "Kali, Kali, my passionate, intriguing, maddening mystery woman! Please put me out of my misery and tell me the truth . . ."

"Lang, what are you talking about?"

His hold on her tightened. "Is *conflict of interest* the modern executive woman's way of saying she's falling in love?" he rasped, lifting his head to stare down at her with a hungry, vulnerable expression that made it impossible for her to be anything but honest.

"Are you interested in the love of a modern, executive woman?" she asked, standing very still in his arms.

172

He slid his hands up to either side of her face, tilting her head back. She caught her breath at the burnished emerald heat flaming in his eyes now.

"I don't think I could live without it," he acknowledged with an aching need.

"Oh, Lang . . . !"

"I've loved you from the moment I saw you standing at the foot of the Bryants' stairs. I took one look at the elegant, aloof little robot dressed in black velvet and I knew I'd found the one woman in the world I really wanted to carry off into the night," he told her with such blatant honesty that all of Kali's intuition knew he spoke the truth.

"And instead I carried you off." She smiled in shaky humor. "You'd had too much Scotch to drive, as I recall!" Her smoky eyes were soft with loving.

"Details," he dismissed loftily, his thumbs sensually massaging the edges of her mouth. "I wasn't too drunk to realize I'd found what I wanted. Kali, do you really love me?"

"With all my heart, Lang."

"When you told me on the phone that you were taking yourself out of the negotiations because I'd become a conflict of interest, I panicked. I wasn't at all sure what you meant and then when you said you wanted to be free to come to me without any strings attached I thought I would go out of my head. All I could think of was wrapping up the deal on those damn patents so that you and I could be together. I want you so much, darling. These last few days have been hell!"

"Why were you so restrained these last few days?" she teased gently. "Were you playing games with me, Lang? Trying to unsettle me?"

"And if I was?" he muttered thickly, moving his hands

up through her neatly bound hair, tearing it free as he went.

"You were very successful, if that was your goal," she admitted.

"I only wanted to try and put you in touch with yourself, Kali. I wanted you to admit you needed me, desired me on some level. And I had rushed you into my bed so quickly that I was afraid you'd chalk the whole thing off to physical desire if I didn't give you a chance to think. I didn't dare hope you'd fall in love with me as quickly as I had fallen in love with you but I knew you must feel something important or you wouldn't have let the robot image slip so many times . . ."

"Talk about a manipulator!" she breathed in amused admiration.

He shook his head. "I needed you, wanted you so badly. I would have done just about anything to get you. That first night when I carried you off to bed all I could think of was putting chains on you. I wanted to seduce you so thoroughly you wouldn't be able to think of any other man except me. God! Kali, I've never wanted a woman the way I want you. You make me think of crazy schemes like binding you hand and foot, tossing you over my saddle-bow, and riding off into the night . . ."

"Well, when the DeLorean arrives, perhaps you could toss me into that," she suggested throatily, the excitement his words generated making it difficult to find the light comment.

"You know about that, do you?" he growled.

"I thought I knew everything there was to know about you before I intercepted you on that staircase that night," she whispered.

"And . . . ?"

"And, as it turns out, it was myself I didn't know enough about," she admitted huskily. "How could I guess

174

I would be the sort to fall in love with a man who had the nerve to put romance before business!"

His mouth curved in a devil's smile of passion and his fingers snagged for a long moment in her cascading hair. Then he slid his hands intimately down around her body. There was a moment of pleasant dizziness as he swept her off her feet and high into his arms.

Kali gave herself up to the delicious sensation of being carried off to the bed of the man she loved. Her arms twined around his neck as his lips came down on hers with deep urgency.

In the bedroom he set her gently on her feet, touching her lightly, caressingly, as he slowly removed her glasses and the jacket of her little business suit. She felt the faint tremble of desire in him and she smiled tenderly at the evidence of his loving passion.

"I love you," she whispered, cupping his hard face in her palms and standing on tiptoe to brush his mouth with her own.

"Oh, Kali, my sweet . . ."

Slowly her clothes pooled at her feet as he removed them one by one. When she stood clad in only the scraps of lace that were her bra and panties, Kali put her hands on the lapels of his suit jacket and pushed it off his shoulders. Then, her own fingers trembling now, she went to work on the buttons of his shirt and the striped tie.

He stood, clearly enjoying the act of being undressed by her, his hands running lightly over her nearly nude body as she worked. Now and then he nuzzled her nape, dropping tiny, anticipatory little kisses. When she had bared the crisp, coppery hair on his chest Kali sighed softly, pressing close and wrapping her arms around his waist. Her nails bit lightly into the skin of his back and he drew in his breath.

"I knew the first night that the robot image was only

175

superficial," Lang grated, cupping the curves of her derriere with tender violence.

"You discovered that much before you passed out?"

"Umm. It was my last conscious thought that night and my first conscious one the next morning. Until you flung Wakefield in my face, that is!"

She caught her lower lip between her teeth, lowering her lashes. "You were a little upset at my maneuvering that morning. Not that it seems to have mattered in the long run," she added a bit aggressively. "When you finally decided to get your bidding war going, you did it with a vengeance!"

"Ah, but that little scene in the restaurant this afternoon was as much for your sake as it was mine!"

"Meaning?" she demanded in confusion. She tipped her head back to eye him narrowly.

"Meaning it was for real. How could I do less than show you I was taking your romantic gesture at face value? You had said you would come to me regardless of what happened with the patents and that you didn't want them to be a factor in our relationship. I wanted to make it clear that the patents were strictly a business matter from that point on."

"You were certainly all business in that restaurant!" she groaned, remembering.

"Oh, I fully intended to sell them to the highest bidder and up until the last minute, that meant they were going to Hadley. Wakefield's problem was that he doesn't understand there are other factors involved besides money when one is dealing with a human being."

"If I hadn't thought of the nonmilitary use clause you would have sold those patents to Davis, wouldn't you?"

"Yes. Does that bother you?"

"No," she murmured. "That reassures me. I didn't

176

want you giving me those patents just to get me. I wanted whatever we had together to be . . ."

" . . . free of any conflict of interest?" He smiled.

She nodded.

"When I finally realized that's what you were trying to tell me on the phone I knew I had to get the damned business over with!"

"You can be appallingly efficient when you choose!" Kali skated her fingers lightly inside the waistband of his slacks, loving the feel of his firm, warm skin.

He acknowledged that with a mockingly arched brow and then he deliberately unbuckled the clasp of his belt. Silently, his eyes never leaving hers, he stepped out of the remainder of his clothing and then reached out to remove her bra and panties.

When she would have stepped naked back into his arms, he stopped her gently, his hands curving around her shoulders.

"How soon will you marry me, Kali?"

"Are you asking me?" she breathed, her heart singing. She loved him and she knew he loved her, but still a woman wanted that ultimate commitment.

"Oh, yes. I fully intend to marry you. Didn't you know that in some ways I'm a little old-fashioned?" His eyes flamed as he searched her face.

"Old-fashioned!" She could have laughed at the depths of such an understatement but the fire in his gaze prevented that. The flames were beginning to burn her skin deliciously.

"Umm. Old-fashioned," he confirmed thickly. "Having found the woman I've been looking for all these years, I won't settle for less than full possession, legal and otherwise!"

"How many years have you been searching, Lang?" she asked with the softest of teasing smiles.

"A couple of hundred at least," he muttered. He reached behind her to pull down the covers of the mammoth bed and then once more he lifted her, settling her in the middle of the bed.

He stood looking down at her softness with a kind of wonder which comes exclusively to the male of the species when he finds himself in love completely and absolutely. It was at once a look of possession, hunger, tenderness, and need. It made Kali glow from within and she opened her arms to him with wordless love.

"There will never be anyone else, Kali, my love," Lang swore, lowering himself into her waiting arms and grasping her with rough gentleness.

"No," she agreed. It was the truth. "I'll marry you, my darling Lang. Whenever you wish. I kept telling myself you were born into the wrong era, but perhaps you were put here to rescue me from the era into which I had accidentally been born!"

"It doesn't matter where or when we find ourselves," he growled, tracing her arching throat with his lips. "We make our own world when we're together."

She moaned in the sweetness of a woman's rising passion and the soft sound seemed to enflame him. Lang's possessive touch roved over her body, exploring, arousing, tantalizing.

She thrust against him, aware of the weight of his legs as they tangled and pinned her own. The fierce maleness prodded her thigh and with an exclamation of need she bent to him, her lips tracking warm, damp patterns across the firm lines of his stomach and down to the strong contour of his hip.

"Kali!"

He wound his hands deeply in her hair, groaning huskily as she teased him with her mouth and delicate, butterfly touches of her fingers.

178

She held him intimately, her nails gliding along the inside of his thigh and up to seize him with feminine urgency.

"You're going to drive me out of my mind, my darling," he gritted, suddenly taking hold of her shoulders and pulling her up along his body so that she lay full length on top of him. "Do you have any idea of what you do to me?" he demanded thickly as their eyes locked.

"I want to seduce you," she told him richly, eyes cloudy with desire. "I want you to be as bound to me as I am to you!" Her hands splayed across his chest and she lowered her head to search out his mouth.

He opened his warmth to her at once, letting her exploring tongue probe deeply to find his. And while they played the ancient, provocative game, his hands slid down her back to the fullness of her hips. Then, with tantalizing slowness, he repeated the gesture, stroking her into an impassioned, twisting creature of love.

When she gasped aloud, lifting her head as she arched her body into him, he moved swiftly, sweeping her onto her back and reversing their position. She flung up her arms to cling to him as he came down on top of her.

Then it was his turn to work his way lovingly down the length of her body. Kali moaned again and again as he strung the hot kisses over her breasts, pausing to tempt a nipple and then on down to the small curve of her stomach. Lower he went, sliding between her legs until his teeth lightly savaged the delicate skin of her thighs.

"Lang, oh, please, Lang!"

His fingers clenched deeply into the shape of her calves and then prowled higher and higher until he was probing her close warmth.

Kali's head reeled with the chaos of passionate emotions and she clutched at him, begging him to come to her

179

completely. Still he hesitated, fueling the flames within her ever higher with every touch, every caress.

"Kali, darling . . ." he finally whispered, "I can't wait any longer . . ."

"Oh, yes, now!" she cried softly.

He pulled away from her for a moment, performing the small ritual of protection with one hand while the other continued to stroke her breasts, and then he came to her fully.

Kali's breath seemed locked in her throat for a timeless moment as his thighs pressed heavily against hers, seeking the closest intimacy possible between a man and a woman. She sensed the surging strength of his manhood on the brink of making them one and she waited with mind-spinning expectation, her nails biting into his shoulders.

"Lang?" When he made no further move to complete the union, she lifted her lashes in sensual question.

He was waiting for her. When she opened her eyes and met his gaze fully, he thrust heavily against her. It was as if he wanted that one extra measure of contact binding them. She saw the raging desire in his eyes and was lost completely in the whirlpool which swept them both up and out to sea.

Mindlessly, joyously, she clung to this man from another world who had carried her off into the night. Her senses shimmered with the love that flowed along them, touching every part of her. The tautness of his muscled back beneath her hands, the hardness of his legs as he trapped her ankles and held her firmly beneath him, all seemed to contribute to the spiraling emotion of the moment.

"Kali!"

Her name seemed torn from his throat as he contained her writhing passion within his grasp, urging her to explode beneath him.

And then the violent convulsion took her, sending the

shivers rocketing out to the farthest corners of her mind and body. She called Lang's name over and over again in a breathless voice, clinging to him as if he were all that mattered in her world.

When she opened her eyes once more she again found him waiting for her. He had not left her body, nor had he allowed his own release to take place. Instead he had held her tightly as she found satisfaction and now he waited as she questioned him with a languid, silent gaze.

The taut planes of his face were tightly etched with the lines of his as yet unfulfilled desire and the bronze-green eyes flickered with the promise of what was to happen next.

Drowsy with contentment, not understanding his actions, Kali smiled up into his tense, expectant face, her smoky eyes veiled by sensuously heavy lashes. Playfully she drew small circles along his shoulders, her satisfied body beginning to come down from the high it had so recently experienced.

Then she gasped as he began to move within her again, this time with a forceful, dominating intensity that seemed to block the downward path of her descending senses.

"Lang, no . . . I . . ." Desperately she caught at his shoulders. How could she explain that her whole body was suddenly, unbearably, too sensitized?

"What are you doing?" she whispered, "I . . . I can't stand it!"

"Yes, you can," he rasped, lowering his head to her mouth as the hard rhythm increased. "Give into it, sweetheart. Just give into it!"

Before the unwinding tension within her had even had a chance to relax, it was being drawn irresistibly taut again. Kali had no choice but to let his body dominate hers completely. It was as if every part of her were on fire this time. The ultrasensitized skin would have responded to the lightest of touches; there was no describing its reaction to the heavy, overwhelming mastery it was receiving.

She tried to cry out but he sealed her mouth with his own, swallowing the sound.

And then Kali felt as if she really had gone out of her head. This second convulsion stormed her body completely. She had a vague realization that Lang had followed her this time, giving vent to his own fierce passion as she went wild beneath him.

A long time later, Kali finally managed to stir against the warmth of the lean, hard body next to her.

"Oh, Lang," she groaned against his chest. "I don't think I shall ever be able to move again! What have you done to me?"

She heard his soft chuckle in the vicinity of her ear and then he was carefully disentangling himself, leaving her lying limply in bed as he got a little unsteadily to his feet. She looked up at him in silent, loving accusation and the satisfied, wonderfully buccaneering smile which edged his mouth made her mutter warily beneath her breath.

"Don't go anywhere, sweetheart," he ordered huskily.

"As if I could!"

He headed for the bath and she heard the sound of water rushing into the still-unpaid-for Roman bath. Kali shut her eyes, thinking how blissful the swirling warm water was going to feel. Nor did she open them a few minutes later when Lang returned to the bed and scooped her up.

"Such a wise investment," she murmured as he lowered her into the frothy water. "And to think I had the notion you were spending your future money foolishly! Oh, my God!"

"What's wrong?" he asked, sinking down beside her and pulling her against him. He tilted his head back, eyes closed, his hand moving lazily over her breast under the water.

"I think I'm going to be sore in the morning," she complained, aware of nearly every muscle in her body.

He laughed, sounding pleased. The sound broke off abruptly as she pinched his ribs. "Ouch! Is that any way to treat your future husband?"

"Beast!"

"I just wanted to make you realize you weren't the only one capable of a bit of manipulation!" he explained, sounding aggrieved.

"Making love to a woman until she literally can't move strikes me as a tad primitive." Kali leaned her head back against his shoulder, relaxing completely in the surging water. She flinched as his thumb grazed unexpectedly over a nipple. Every inch of her felt exquisitely sensitive still. At such a level of awareness there was a very fine line between pleasure and pain. She *was* going to be sore in the morning, damn it!

"I suppose it is. A tad." He sounded gloriously complacent about the fact. "But when a man is dealing with a rather primitive woman, that's the only sensible approach to use."

"Primitive! Me! You're the throwback here, not me!"

He laughed again, snuggling her close. "I've got news for you, honey. I knew I was going to have to tame you in my bed the moment I saw you. I took one look into those smoky eyes of yours and I knew I was dealing with the kind of woman who would respond best to being carried off into the night. Ideal situation for me, you know," he confided. "I needed a woman like that. We were probably fated to meet," he concluded with a shrug, accepting his future with her completely.

Kali's legs moved languidly under the water as she turned carefully on her side to face him. "Would you have

183

really forced me to come to you in exchange for those patents?" she demanded interestedly.

He stroked the line of her cheek and then touched her breast, a smile edging his hard mouth. "Yes. I would have used whatever means was necessary to get you."

"Regardless of how much I was going to have IAI pay for them?" she pressed deliberately. "You proved you're a businessman when you want to be, Lang. Would you really have just handed those patents over to IAI in return for my agreement to come to you?"

"I'm capable of doing business when the occasion demands it," he murmured deeply, caressing her nipple almost absently between thumb and forefinger. "But when it comes to you, I have other priorities. I would have handed over the patents or anything else I thought might lure you into my clutches."

She shook her head, awed by the undeniable force of his emotion. "Oh, Lang, I'll try to make you happy, I swear it . . . !"

"You already have," he told her simply, dropping a damp kiss on her nose. "Will you mind being married to a would-be writer of science fiction? I understand they're inclined to be eccentric and irrational at times."

"Is that so? Any more eccentric and irrational than inventors?"

"I don't know. Are inventors all that bad?" He chuckled.

"Well, I really can't speak for inventors in general," she demurred, "but as far as roboticists go . . ."

"Yes?" he prompted, tugging her across his thighs and cradling her into his shoulder.

"Roboticists," she explained kindly, "can drive a woman crazy."

"Ah, well. Lady executives can be a bit trying, too, at times." He nodded easily. His hand began straying under-

184

water along her body. "But that's all right. I know how to handle them now. Or, at least, I know how to handle one particular lady executive now!" he corrected feelingly. He touched her knee and Kali arched it instinctively at the small caress. Under the frothy water her toes curled tightly.

"How?" she provoked, her arms circling his neck.

"I'll be giving you plenty of practical demonstrations in the future. Just be sure you pay attention."

"Oh, I will," she assured him in tones of deepest admiration. "After all, everyone keeps telling me you're a genius."

"In my field," he amended modestly, lowering his mouth until it hovered only an inch from her parted lips.

"Robotics?"

"You," he stated decisively, "are my new field of specialization."

He took her lips with the promise of several lifetimes, past, present, and future.

LOOK FOR NEXT MONTH'S
CANDLELIGHT ECSTASY ROMANCES ®

Seize The Dawn

by Vanessa Royall

For as long as she could remember, Elizabeth Rolfson knew that her destiny lay in America. She arrived in Chicago in 1885, the stunning heiress to a vast empire. As men of daring pressed westward, vying for the land, Elizabeth was swept into the savage struggle. Driven to learn the secret of her past, to find the one man who could still the restlessness of her heart, she would stand alone against the mighty to claim her proud birthright and grasp a dream of undying love.

A DELL BOOK   17788-X $3.50

THE SEEDS OF SINGING

by Kay McGrath

To the primitive tribes of New Guinea, the seeds of singing are the essence of courage. To Michael Stanford and Catherine Morgan, two young explorers on a lost expedition, they symbolize a passion that defies war, separation, and time itself. In the unmapped highlands beyond the jungle, in a world untouched since the dawn of time, Michael and Catherine discover a passion men and women everywhere only dream about, a love that will outlast everything.

A DELL BOOK   19120-3 $3.95

Desert Hostage

Diane Dunaway

Behind her is England and her first innocent encounter with love. Before her is a mysterious land of forbidding majesty. Kidnapped, swept across the deserts of Araby, Juliette Barclay sees her past vanish in the endless, shifting sands. Desperate and defiant, she seeks escape only to find harrowing danger, to discover her one hope in the arms of her captor, the Shiek of El Abadan. Fearless and proud, he alone can tame her. She alone can possess his soul. Between them lies the secret that will bind her to him forever, a woman possessed, a slave of love.

A DELL BOOK   11963-4 $3.95

Bestsellers

☐ **ELIZABETH TAYLOR: The Last Star**
  by Kitty Kelley...$3.95 (12410-7)

☐ **THE LEGACY** by Howard Fast....................$3.95 (14719-0)

☐ **LUCIANO'S LUCK** by Jack Higgins............$3.50 (14321-7)

☐ **MAZES AND MONSTERS** by Rona Jaffe...$3.50 (15699-8)

☐ **TRIPLETS** by Joyce Rebeta-Burditt............$3.95 (18943-8)

☐ **BABY** by Robert Lieberman.........................$3.50 (10432-7)

☐ **CIRCLES OF TIME** by Phillip Rock.............$3.50 (11320-2)

☐ **SWEET WILD WIND** by Joyce Verrette......$3.95 (17634-4)

☐ **BREAD UPON THE WATERS**
  by Irwin Shaw..$3.95 (10845-4)

☐ **STILL MISSING** by Beth Gutcheon............$3.50 (17864-9)

☐ **NOBLE HOUSE** by James Clavell..............$5.95 (16483-4)

☐ **THE BLUE AND THE GRAY**
  by John Leekley...$3.50 (10631-1)

At your local bookstore or use this handy coupon for ordering:

Dell DELL BOOKS
P.O. BOX 1000, PINE BROOK, N.J. 07058-1000

Please send me the books I have checked above. I am enclosing $ _____ [please add 75c per copy to
cover postage and handling]. Send check or money order—no cash or C.O.D.'s. Please allow up to 8 weeks for
shipment.

Mr./Mrs./Miss _____

Address _____

City _____ State/Zip _____